MW00776434

CAPTIVE HUSBANDRY AND PROPAGATION OF THE BOA CONSTRICTORS AND RELATED BOAS

Captive Husbandry and Propagation of the Boa Constrictors and Related Boas

by David Fogel

KRIEGER PUBLISHING COMPANY
MALABAR, FLORIDA
1997

Original Edition 1997

Printed and Published by
KRIEGER PUBLISHING COMPANY
KRIEGER DRIVE
MALABAR, FLORIDA 32950

Copyright © 1997 by Krieger Publishing Company

Library of Congress Cataloging-In-Publication Data

Fogel, David, 1960–
    Captive husbandry and propagation of the boa constrictors and related boas / by David Fogel. — Original ed.
        p.   cm.
    Includes bibliographical references (p.   ) and index.
    ISBN 0-89464-921-3 (hardcover : alk. paper)
    1. Boa (Genus)—Breeding.   2. Boa (Genus)—Reproduction.
3. Captive snakes—Breeding.   4. Captive snakes—Reproduction.
5. Snake culture.   I. Title
SF515.5.S64F64   1997
639.3'96—dc20   96-46110
                                                                      CIP

10   9   8   7   6   5   4   3   2

Dedicated to my grandfather Bert Meyer,
a gentleman who has overcome much adversity.
His wisdom and accomplishments have
been an inspiration to me.

CONTENTS

COLOR ILLUSTRATIONS

PREFACE

The common Colombian boa constrictor (*Boa constrictor constrictor*) has historically been among the most popular pet snakes in the United States. Tens of thousands are sold through pet shops annually. During the early 1970s a typical retail pet shop could be found pricing baby common Colombian boas at only $9.99 each. At that time every baby boa encountered was a wild-caught specimen, and it was believed that captive propagation of a tropical snake was next to impossible. Twenty years later captive reproduction of many boa species is fairly commonplace.

The commercial value of many snakes has grown substantially with the success of captive propagation. At the top of the list are the boids. Tens of thousands of dollars have been paid by breeders for a single albino or leucistic boid specimen. Now, as with champion dog or horse breeds, snake progeny may offer great financial rewards.

In the early 1970s a pet shop I frequented in Skokie, Illinois, maintained an adult blackheaded python (*Aspidites melanocephalus*). The price tag attached to the terrarium which housed the exotic snake read "unobtainable." Due to the species' rarity and attractiveness, the shop intended the python for display purposes only. I returned to the pet shop several months after my initial viewing and the blackheaded python was still being housed in the same terrarium, the only difference was the price tag. Where it had once read "unobtainable" it now read $600. The reasoning of the pet shop management was that, since so many customers had asked the price of the python, they tagged the snake with what at the time was a ridiculously inflated price. I was informed by the management that as much as they would have liked to retain the python as a display specimen, they reasoned that if someone were crazy enough to pay $600 for a snake, they would be happy to sell it. To the best of my knowledge the python never sold. Today a comparable specimen would command a price of $15,000 to $20,000 from a breeder working with *Aspidites melanocephalus*. One successful breeding could net five times the initial investment in the sale of progeny.

As with any potentially lucrative endeavor, great advances have been made in the field of herpetoculture. Many products are now being commercially manufactured specifically for captive reptiles, including plastic cages, heating devices, and hide boxes. Computerized environmental chambers are utilized to re-create seasonal temperature, photoperiod, and humidity variations which take place in the wild.

The dissemination of knowledge has also become paramount, and herpetoculturists are sharing their knowledge through literature. This practice may have begun with what I believe to be the first book on captive herp husbandry, *The Vivarium*, written by Rev. Gregory C. Bateman in 1897. Today dozens of books and full color periodicals are in print, as well as annual international herpetological symposia on this subject one hundred years later.

Fortunately, dollars and cents are not the prime motivating factors in all cases. Many herpetoculturists maintain collections for the sheer enjoyment and knowledge derived from their captives. With the alarming degree of worldwide habitat destruction, many species of reptiles may depend upon captive propagation in order to survive.

This volume deals specifically with the boas. A diverse group of both New and Old World snakes, boa species and subspecies currently number in excess of one hundred. Adult specimens of certain sand boas (genus *Eryx*) attain a maximum length of only 2–3 feet, while the green anaconda (*Eunectes murinus*) may exceed 30 feet in length. Boa habitat runs the gamut from the upper canopy of tropical rainforest to beneath desert sands.

The primary purpose of this volume is to describe captive husbandry and propagation methods which are being successfully employed by today's keepers. Although all species of boas are included, the main focus is on the species or subspecies which are being maintained (either by zoological institutions or private individuals) in the greatest numbers. The boa species are grouped by geographic distribution, and the more frequently maintained species are addressed at the beginning of each geographic section. In the color section, the represented species appear in the same grouped sequence as mentioned in the text. My hope is that by providing valuable husbandry and propagation information a greater number of captive boas will thrive and reproduce.

ACKNOWLEDGMENTS

I would like to thank everyone who put forth the time and effort to contribute to this volume. The following individuals' generosity greatly added to the project:

Dick Goergen (Alden, New York), Donald Hamper (Columbus, Ohio), Sean McKeown (Chaffee Zoological Gardens, Fresno, California), Valerie Hornyak (Toledo Zoological Society), and Quentin Bloxam (Jersey Wildlife Preservation Trust) contributed valuable boa reproduction data or shared captive husbandry practices.

Paul Gritis (Paul Gritis Natural History Books, Bethlehem, Pennsylvania and Joe Dinardo (Herptitles, Levittown, Pennsylvania) provided needed literature, as well as advice which aided in manuscript preparation.

Dick Goergen, Donald Hamper, Sean McKeown, John H. Tashjian (San Marcos, California), Carl May (Lake Worth, Florida), Al Baldogo (Baldogo Reptiles, Fontanelle, Iowa), Stephen Chandler (Alberta, Canada), Kevin and Sue Hanley (Peoria, Arizona), Stephen Hammack (HISS, Fort Worth, Texas), Peter J. Stafford (The Natural History Museum, London), and Robert Henderson (Milwaukee Public Museum, Wisconsin) contributed photographs. A special thanks to my brother, Bill Fogel (Bill Fogel Photography, University Heights, Ohio), for the many hours spent photographing specimens solely as a favor to me.

Tom Dotson, D.V.M. (Knoxville, Tennessee) brought parties together.

My wife, Anna, helped with the typing of the manuscript. My children Jennifer Fogel and David Manke Jr., helped with proofreading and running errands. I would also like to thank my grandparents, Bert and Sonia Meyer, for their financial help which aided in the acquisition of the Herp House facility; my parents, Sy and Ruth Fogel; and my sister Ellen who indulged me in a hobby which began over two decades ago.

SECTION 1
TAXONOMY

The taxonomy of several species of the Boidae has recently undergone controversial revision. For example, Kluge (1991) places *Xenoboa cropanii* in *Corallus* as *Corallus cropanii*. In addition Kluge reclassifies the Madagascan boas by changing *Sanzinia madagascariensis* to *Boa manditra*, *Acrantophis madagascariensis* to *Boa madagascariensis*, and *Acrantophis dumerili* to *Boa dumerili*. *Boa constrictor* completes the genus. As captive care and propagation is the primary focus of this volume, it is not my intent to confuse the reader by use of new and unfamiliar taxonomic names. The nomenclature used within this volume is that most widely accepted at the time of manuscript preparation.

TAXONOMIC CHECKLIST

The following is a checklist of scientific and common names of the boas. As some of the species or subspecies were described from only a few specimens, their validity may be in question.

Acrantophis dumerili	Dumeril's boa
Acrantophis madagascariensis	Madagascar ground boa
Boa constrictor amarali	Bolivian red-tail boa
Boa constrictor constrictor	Common boa constrictor
Boa constrictor imperator	Mexican boa constrictor
Boa constrictor longicauda	Black boa; Long-tail boa
Boa constrictor melanogaster	Black-bellied boa
Boa constrictor nebulosus	Clouded boa
Boa constrictor occidentalis	Argentine boa constrictor
Boa constrictor orophias	St. Lucia boa
Boa constrictor ortoni	Peruvian red-tail boa

1

Boa constrictor sabogae	Saboga Island boa
Candoia aspera	New Guinea viper boa
Candoia bibroni australis	Solomon Islands tree boa
Candoia bibroni bibroni	Fiji Islands boa
Candoia carinata carinata	Pacific ground boa
Candoia carinata paulsoni	Solomon Islands ground boa
Casarea dussumieri	Round Island boa
Charina bottae bottae	Pacific rubber boa
Charina bottae umbratica	Southern California rubber boa
Charina bottae utahensis	Great Basin rubber boa
Corallus annulatus annulatus	Annulated boa
Corallus annulatus blombergi	Ecuadorian annulated boa
Corallus annulatus colombianus	Colombian annulated boa
Corallus caninus	Emerald tree boa
Corallus enydris cooki	Cook's tree boa
Corallus enydris enydris	Amazon tree boa
Epicrates angulifer	Cuban boa
Epicrates cenchria alvarezi	Argentine rainbow boa
Epicrates cenchria assisi	Caatinga rainbow boa
Epicrates cenchria barbouri	Marajo Island rainbow boa
Epicrates cenchria cenchria	Brazilian rainbow boa
Epicrates cenchria crassus	Paraguayan rainbow boa
Epicrates cenchria gaigei	Peruvian rainbow boa
Epicrates cenchria hygrophilus	Eastern rainbow boa
Epicrates cenchria maurus	Colombian rainbow boa
Epicrates cenchria polylepis	Central Highlands rainbow boa
Epicrates cenchria xerophilus	Rio Branco rainbow boa
Epicrates chrysogaster chrysogaster	Turk's Island boa
Epicrates chrysogaster relicquus	Great Inagua Island boa
Epicrates chrysogaster schwartzi	Acklins Island boa
Epicrates exsul	Abaco Island boa
Epicrates fordi agametus	Mole St. Nicholas ground boa
Epicrates fordi fordi	Ford's boa
Epicrates gracilis gracilis	Haitian vine boa
Epicrates gracilis hapalus	Coastal vine boa

Epicrates inornatus	Puerto Rican boa
Epicrates monensis granti	Virgin Islands boa
Epicrates monensis monensis	Mona Island boa
Epicrates striatus ailurus	Cat Island boa
Epicrates striatus exagistus	Tiburon Peninsula boa
Epicrates striatus fosteri	Bimini Island boa
Epicrates striatus fowleri	Andros Island boa; Berry Island boa
Epicrates striatus mccraniei	Ragged Island boa
Epicrates striatus striatus	Haitian boa
Epicrates striatus strigulatus	Nassau boa
Epicrates striatus warreni	Ile de la Tortue boa
Epicrates subflavus	Jamaican boa
Eryx colubrinus colubrinus	Egyptian sand boa
Eryx colubrinus loveridgei	Kenyan sand boa
Eryx conicus brevis	Sri Lanka sand boa
Eryx conicus conicus	Rough-scaled sand boa
Eryx elegans	Central Asia sand boa
Eryx jaculus familiarus	Caucasian sand boa
Eryx jaculus jaculus	Javelin sand boa
Eryx jaculus turcicus	Turkish sand boa
Eryx jayakari	Arabian sand boa
Eryx johni johni	Smooth-scaled sand boa
Eryx johni persicus	Northern smooth-scaled sand boa
Eryx miliaris	Dwarf sand boa
Eryx muelleri muelleri	Eastern Sahara sand boa
Eryx muelleri subniger	Western Sahara sand boa
Eryx nogaiorum	Black sand boa
Eryx somalicus	Somalian sand boa
Eryx tataricus speciosus	Mountain sand boa
Eryx tataricus tataricus	Tartar sand boa
Eryx tataricus vittatus	Striped sand boa
Eunectes barbouri	Marajo Island anaconda
Eunectes deschauenseei	Dark-spotted anaconda
Eunectes murinus gigas	Northern green anaconda
Eunectes murinus murinus	Southern green anaconda
Eunectes notaeus	Yellow anaconda
Exiliboa placata	Oaxacan dwarf boa

Lichanura trivirgata myriolepis	Southern California rosy boa
Lichanura trivirgata roseofusca	Desert rosy boa
Lichanura trivirgata saslowi	Mid-Baja rosy boa
Lichanura trivirgata trivirgata	Mexican rosy boa
Sanzinia madagascariensis	Madagascar tree boa
Trachyboa boulengeri	Northern eyelash boa
Trachyboa gularis	Southern eyelash boa
Tropidophis battersbyi	Ecuador dwarf boa
Tropidophis canus androsi	Andros Island dwarf boa
Tropidophis canus barbouri	Eastern Bahama Islands dwarf boa
Tropidophis canus canus	Great Inagua Island dwarf boa
Tropidophis canus curtus	Bimini Island dwarf boa
Tropidophis caymanensis caymanensis	Grand Cayman dwarf boa
Tropidophis caymanensis parkeri	Little Cayman dwarf boa
Tropidophis caymanensis schwartzi	Cayman Brac Island dwarf boa
Tropidophis feicki	Western Cuba banded dwarf boa
Tropidophis greenwayi greenwayi	Ambergris Cay dwarf boa
Tropidophis greenwayi lanthanus	Caicos Island dwarf boa
Tropidophis haetianus haetianus	Haitian dwarf boa
Tropidophis haetianus hemerus	East Hispaniola dwarf boa
Tropidophis haetianus jamaicensis	Southern Jamaica dwarf boa
Tropidophis haetianus stejnegeri	Northern Jamaica dwarf boa
Tropidophis haetianus stulli	Portland Point dwarf boa
Tropidophis haetianus tiburonensis	Tiburon dwarf boa
Tropidophis maculatus	Spotted dwarf boa
Tropidophis melanurus bucculentus	Navassa Island black-tailed dwarf boa
Tropidophis melanurus dysodes	Isla de Pinos dwarf boa
Tropidophis melanurus eriksoni	Isla de Pinos black-tailed dwarf boa
Tropidophis melanurus melanurus	Cuban black-tailed dwarf boa
Tropidophis nigriventris hardyi	Hardy's black-bellied dwarf boa

Tropidophis nigriventris nigriventris	Black-bellied dwarf boa
Tropidophis pardalis	Leopard dwarf boa
Tropidophis paucisquamis	Brazilian [or] Peruvian dwarf boa
Tropidophis pilsbryi galacelidus	Sierra de Trinidad dwarf boa
Tropidophis pilsbryi pilsbryi	Pilsbry's dwarf boa
Tropidophis semicinctus	Banded dwarf boa
Tropidophis taczanowski	Western South America dwarf boa
Tropidophis wrighti	Eastern Cuba dwarf boa
Ungaliophis continentalis	Chipan boa
Ungaliophis panamensis	Panamanian dwarf boa
Xenoboa cropanii	Sao Paulo boa

SECTION 2
HUSBANDRY

DESIGNING A HERP ROOM

There comes a time when the typical herpetoculturist's boa collection becomes so extensive that it necessitates a room or rooms specifically designed to maintain herps. Herp rooms allow fine tuning of ambient temperature, humidity, and photoperiod. Well-constructed facilities provide security for the captive herps, herp keeper, and neighboring individuals who may or may not be reptile enthusiasts.

The first consideration for the herp room should be location. Herp rooms can be located either above or below ground, with each having certain advantages and disadvantages. When herp rooms are constructed below ground level they are naturally insulated by tons of earth, and desired temperatures can be maintained with minimal energy expenditures. The disadvantages to subterranean rooms are the possibility of water seepage and the difficulty in providing ventilation. Any rooms which are constructed below ground should be equipped with a sump pit and sump pump to remove unwanted water which may accumulate on the floor from seepage. Herp rooms which are located above ground rarely pose flooding problems, but can be expensive to heat and cool in geographic areas where temperature extremes occur.

Existing rooms can be converted to function as herp rooms, but the most functional one will be a room specifically designed and constructed to maintain herps. Prior to construction a detailed floor plan and materials list should be composed. Various materials may be used in the construction of herp rooms. The most common material for wall construction is standard 2 × 4 in wood studs. Metal studs (most often used in commercial applications) can also be considered, but present some problems, such as fastening shelving to them. Moisture resistant drywall and T-1-11 exterior grade wood siding are good choices as wall material, especially in tropical rooms where relative humidity is high. If the wall studs are set in metal track, the possibility of water damage to the walls can be lessened by providing a ¾ inch gap between the floor and the bottom of the wall. Vinyl base molding can be applied to the bottom of walls to seal out moisture.

Insulation should be added to the walls of any room which is being heated or cooled. Fiberglass, loose cellulose, and stiff foam board are all effective insulators. A vapor barrier should be installed on the warm side of the room over all insulation. Plastic sheeting with a minimum thickness of 6 mils works well, as does kraft paper, which is often attached to one side of fiberglass insulation. Ceilings should also be insulated to prevent heat loss from the room in cold weather, and excessive heat gain in the room in warm weather. Electrical outlet and light switch boxes can also be insulated by installing manufactured insulating pads behind the switch and outlet covers. In geographic areas that experience extreme cold, windows can be a source of considerable heat loss and should be avoided or kept to a minimum in herp rooms. Consideration should be given to the nmber and placement of electrical outlets. Additional circuits and possibly circuit boxes may have to be installed. If electric heaters are to be used, circuits exclusively for their use should be available. Light switches controlling the primary room lighting should be located outside of the herp room entrance. This will allow the lights to be turned on before entering the room. If there has been an escape during the evening, a potentially dangerous situation may be avoided. A qualified electrician should be consulted for all wiring projects.

Overhead room lighting is a wise choice for herp rooms, as no floor space is wasted with lamps. Fluorescent light fixtures equipped with the appropriate wattage lamps provide good economical illumination. Emergency lights should be installed in all herp rooms which house large, potentially dangerous boids or venomous species. Emergency lights which activate when a power outage occurs may prevent an accident in total darkness.

Herp room doors should be wide enough to accommodate large boid enclosures. An approximately 1 m (36 in) or 81 cm (32 in) wide standard door will usually suffice. Long straight aisles leading to all herp room doors should be provided to facilitate the moving of large enclosures.

Large wash trays with both hot and cold water should be located in convenient locations within the herp rooms. Soap and hand towel dispensers should be mounted near each wash tray.

The herp room floor can consist of any material from bare concrete to hardwood. The main consideration is that the floor be relatively waterproof and easy to maintain. Linoleum and vinyl floor coverings are often a good choice.

All herp rooms should be escape proof. Even the smallest cracks and openings should be sealed. This will prevent hatchling and neonate herps from exiting the room should they escape from their enclosures. Sink drain openings should be covered with a strainer or wire mesh to prevent escapes through the plumbing. Large boids have the ability to scale walls and enter suspended ceilings by displacing ceiling tiles. Special clips are available to hold suspended ceiling tiles securely in place.

Multiple herp rooms can be very beneficial. Separate rooms for tropical and temperate region species allow various ambient temperatures to be maintained. A tropical room can provide an ambient temperature of 26°C (80°F), while an adjoining room can be maintained at 13°C (55°F) for hibernating temperate region species. Relative humidity and photoperiod can also be manipulated to meet the specific needs of each room's inhabitants. A separate room in which temperature cycling is not being incorporated and constant temperatures are being maintained is beneficial for growing juvenile herps to sexual maturity.

Heating for the herp room is a top priority in most geographic regions. There are several varieties of room heating devices one may choose. The most convenient and easiest to install is electric heat. Electric heat comes in many forms, such as baseboard, overhead mounted, and portable models. Electric baseboard heater installation consists of mounting the heaters at the bottom of the walls at various intervals. This results in the loss of wall space for shelving, large enclosures, enclosure racks, etc. Freestanding portable floor model electric heaters may consist of quartz elements, oil-filled units resembling radiators on wheels, or small ceramic units. Portable heaters occupy a small amount of floor space and must not be positioned too close to herp enclosures or any flammable material. Some portable electric heaters achieve external cabinet temperatures which can be a burn hazard to herps and herp keepers. Portable electric heaters equipped with a fan for circulating warm air will aid in providing a uniform ambient room temperature.

Natural gas and liquid propane-fueled heaters are also effective for heating herp rooms. These units usually require venting to the outside of the building.

An accurate, heavy duty thermostat should be connected to any heat source. See Figure 1. The location of the thermostat within the herp room is very important. The height at which the thermostat is mounted will influence ambient room temperature. It is not unusual for the ambient air temperature to be several degrees warmer at eye level than at floor level. Thermostats should not be located in areas where they will be subjected to drafts, such as near entryways or windows. A clear plastic thermostat cover can be used to guard against the temperature setting being accidentally altered.

An accurate maximum-minimum thermometer should be present in every herp room. See Figure 2. This type of thermometer not only displays the current temperature reading, but also records the highest and lowest temperatures which have occurred within the room. A temperature alarm can also be installed to warn of excessively high or low ambient room temperatures caused by heater or air conditioner failure.

Relative humidity should be controlled within various herp rooms. It may be necessary to include a humidifier in rooms which house tropical herps. A hygrometer should be used to monitor relative humidity levels in all herp rooms.

Air conditioning may be necessary to keep herp rooms at the required temperatures during the summer months. Most air conditioning units will remove moisture (thereby affecting relative humidity) along with the warm air, and may present problems for tropical boas.

A well-designed interior layout of a herp room can make

 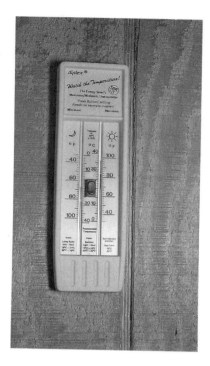

Figure 1 This accurate, heavy-duty thermostat can be used to regulate a 110 volt room heater. Courtesy of Bill Fogel Photography.

Figure 2 A maximum-minimum thermometer is an effective tool for monitoring the current ambient temperature within a herp room, as well as recording the highest and lowest temperatures realized within the room. Courtesy of Bill Fogel Photography.

daily maintenance more efficient and less hazardous. Shelving units make effective use of a room's vertical space. Shelving can consist of wall-mounted boards secured with metal angle brackets, or wood cleats and posts. Freestanding portable shelving units can be located anywhere throughout the herp room. Enclosures can be placed back-to-back on freestanding shelves to maximize floor space. Racks can also be constructed to house multiple shoebox or sweaterbox enclosures. Always allow adequate aisle space between shelving, herp enclosures, etc., to allow for safe movement while performing maintenance. This is especially important when working with potentially dangerous species. Safety dictates that large boids and venomous species be maintained within enclosures located on lower level shelving.

A well-illuminated counter or table where herps can be examined, probed, etc., should be incorporated into the herp room. If the counter is located near the wash tray it can also be used for food preparation and easily disinfected.

A negative ion generator or alternative air filtration system is a useful addition to any herp room, as it can eliminate the majority of airborne pollutants and odors. Water filtration can also be beneficial to herps. Carbon block water filtration units are effective when used in conjunction with municipal water systems, as they remove chlorine. Reverse osmosis filtration units are a good choice for providing pure water from municipal water systems, wells, etc., as chlorine, toxins, and heavy metals are removed.

An emergency generator, fueled by gasoline, natural gas, or liquid propane, should be available to maintain proper temperatures in the event of a power outage. A transfer switch can be wired from the generator directly to an electrical service box to activate the desired electrical circuits when the generator is operating. A less expensive alternative is to hardwire emergency electrical outlets within the herp room with the wires' opposite ends being plugged directly into the generator's outlets. If the generator does not have an automatic start feature, a power outage alarm can alert the keeper to manually start the generator.

HEATING DEVICES AND THEIR APPLICATION TO HERPETOCULTURE

Boas, like all reptiles, are cold-blooded (poikilothermic) and must rely on their environment to regulate body temperature. In temperate areas additional heat must be provided throughout winter months for captive tropical boas as well as temperate area boas which are not being hibernated.

In the early 1970s I relied on Metaframe stainless steel hoods containing the appropriate wattage incandescent light bulbs to achieve 80+°F temperatures (28°C) within boa terraria. During cold winters the lights continued to burn day and night, week after week. Although this method did provide tropical temperatures it did not duplicate photoperiods, and it was extremely inefficient. Now a variety of heating devices are being successfully incorporated into reptile enclosures.

It is important to keep in mind some heating basics. Heat rises. This is an important consideration when choosing heating devices for specific enclosures. The ambient temperature where boas are being housed will be an important factor when choosing heating devices. As discussed earlier, heating an entire well-insulated room can be a worthwhile investment when maintaining a large boa collection. Additional enclosure heating devices must be considered to allow for individual boa thermoregulation.

There are also several factors within a given enclosure which can affect temperature. The amount of ventilation, the material of which the enclosure is constructed, the size of the enclosure, and the type of substrate all influence enclosure temperature. Captive boas must be given the opportunity to thermoregulate. The boa will know its optimal temperature requirements better than the boa keeper. If the boa has recently fed, is nearing ecdysis, or is gravid, then warmer than average temperatures are needed. Therefore, a thermal gradient, which provides warmer and cooler areas within the same enclosure, must be provided for boas. For boa species requiring hide areas, the enclosure should be equipped with shelters located throughout the thermal gradient. This will allow the boa to move from warmer to cooler areas and remain sheltered. If multiple shelters are not provided, some boas will choose the security of a shelter at the cost of enduring sub-optimal temperatures.

Substrate Heating

Pipe heat tapes are typically about 13 mm (½ in) wide, and 3 mm (⅛ in) thick. Tapes range in length from 1 m (3 ft) to over 34 m (100 ft). They are designed for wrapping water pipes to prevent freezing. See Figure 3.

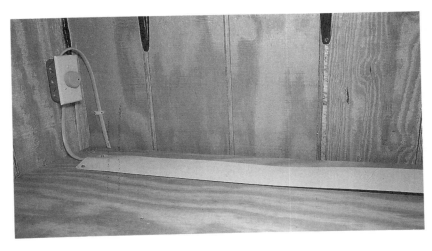

Figure 3 A pipe heat tape beneath 4 inch wide aluminum flashing and wired to a dimmer switch is effective supplemental substrate heat for enclosures supported by long shelves. Courtesy of Bill Fogel Photography.

Pipe heat tapes are most effective when affixed to long lengths of shelving which support a number of enclosures. In this application the tape can be covered with an appropriate width strip of aluminum flashing for better heat dissipation. The tape should be run along the rear third of the shelf to allow boas to thermoregulate by moving from the front to the rear of the enclosure. Pipe heat tapes can also be used effectively in upright shelving units, such as those that utilize shoebox, sweater-box, or Rubbermaid containers. In this application lengths of tape can be run across the top shelf, down the side of the unit to the next shelf, down the opposite side of the unit to the next shelf, and so on until all shelves are covered.

In large units several tapes should be used (one per every few shelves) for added control. When using pipe heat tapes with wooden units a dado groove can be cut with a router bit or tablesaw blade in which the tape can be recessed for a flush fit. When heat tapes are being used with wooden shelves, I have covered the top surface of the shelf with vinyl flooring. This prevents a fire hazard and also waterproofs the shelf.

Another option is to run the length of tape through 19–25 mm (¾–1 in) diameter copper pipe, which can also be filled with sand to increase heated mass beneath the cage floor.

Pipe heat tapes draw 7 watts per foot and must be wired to a rheostat or dimmer switch to allow for precise temperature control. These can be wired directly into the non-heating lead of the heat tape. An alternative method of control (which requires no electrical knowledge) is to plug the tape directly into a ready made "dimmer box."

The heat tapes must be the variety without a built-in thermostat which typically activates the tape at about 4°C (40°F). Cox Premium Series heat cables are the finest tapes I have used. Unfortunately, they are no longer being manufactured. Smith Gates Easy Heat heat cables seem to be the best alternative. The only drawback to pipe heat tape is that it can not be cut to size, and tapes are not available in many intermediate lengths. Pipe heat tapes are heavy duty and long-lived. I highly recommend them.

Flex-watt heat tape is an almost paper thin tape available in various widths. Its composition is heating wire sealed within plastic. Flex-watt is manufactured for the horticultural industry. It is designed to be buried beneath soil to warm plant roots.

Flex-watt heat tape is widely used among herpetoculturists. The main benefit of this type of tape is that it can be easily cut to any length and lies flat in most applications. Rheostats or dimmers should be used in conjunction with Flex-watt.

The drawback is that for every section of tape cut from the 152 m (500 ft) roll a crimped electrical connection must be made and an additional length of electrical cord provided. The opposite end of the tape must be sealed. Due to the thin construction of Flex-watt, it is comparatively delicate. My experience has been that as the tape aged, cold spots formed at irregular intervals.

Galvanized metal heat pads designed to heat small animal nest boxes are available in two sizes: 33 × 53 cm (13 × 21 in) and 23 × 43 cm (9 × 17 in). The pads consist of a waterproof heating element sandwiched between two thin galvanized steel plates. A heavy duty cord and grounded plug exit the center of one end of the pad. See Figure 4.

There are many benefits to this type of heat pad. The entire

Figure 4 Galvanized metal heat pads can be used as supplemental substrate heat for individual enclosures. Courtesy of Bill Fogel Photography.

surface of the pad heats evenly. The electrical consumption is only 20 watts. The pads are weather resistant, and no rheostat or dimmer switch is required. Galvanized heat pads are among the most reasonably priced of the herp heating devices.

The best application of the metal pad is to position it under the enclosure. This eliminates the need to drill a hole in the enclosure or enclosure top through which to run the electrical cord. With the pad outside of the enclosure it is maintenance free (no cleaning). The heat from the pad will radiate through glass or wood bottom enclosures. Metal pads are also ideally suited for use with fiberglass or plastic enclosures such as Neodesha. Pad placement should be such that no more than one-third to one-half of the enclosure floor area is being heated. This will allow the inhabitants to thermoregulate by moving on or off the heated area as needed.

Galvanized metal heat pads are extremely durable and long-lived. I have extensive experience with these pads and highly recommend them, and I hope in the near future a larger size will be available as well.

Fiberglass heat pads, designed to heat pigs, are available in six sizes ranging from 30 × 46 cm (12 × 18 in) to 61 × 122 cm (2 × 4 ft). Fiberglass pads are considerably thicker than the galvanized pads, and consume much more electricity. The main benefit to the fiberglass heat pad is the availability of large sizes, ideally suited for large boid enclosures.

In most applications the pads require a rheostat, or temperature control unit. Mounting holes are provided at the pad corners which allow the pad to be screwed directly to the bottom of wooden enclosures. The fiberglass heat pads can be used in many of the same applications as galvanized pads, but are not as reasonably priced. "Pig heater" pads work well and are recommended.

In enclosures with deep substrate, i.e., several inches of soil or sand, either of the previously mentioned heat pads may be buried in the substrate to an appropriate depth.

Hot Rocks, introduced in the mid 1970s, were specifically designed for heating reptiles. The original Hot Rocks consisted of a brick with an 8 ohm, 10 watt resistor cemented in the center and connected to an electrical cord which existed through the end of the brick. Hot Rocks of all varieties do warm to an effective temperature. Unfortunately, the materials used in the construction of Hot Rocks do not dissipate heat well. This causes a small area of the rock to become too hot and other portions of the rock to remain cool. Compared to heat pads Hot Rocks have far less surface area to volume ratio. There have been documented cases of thermal burns in reptiles resulting from the use of Hot Rocks. Hot Rocks can not be used effectively outside of the enclosure.

There is no application where any form of Hot Rocks can be utilized as effectively as heat pads or heat tapes. Hot Rocks have become obsolete and primarily a pet shop item. I do not recommend their use by serious herpetoculturists.

Adhesive heat pads are designed to stick to the bottom of herp cages. These pads are small with little surface area. I have corresponded with individuals who have reported that adhesive heat pads have become so hot that they they cracked the glass bottom of terraria and warped or melted plastic herp enclosures. As with Hot Rocks these are primarily sold to beginning herpetoculturists. I do not recommend their use.

Overhead Heating

Spotlight bulbs in the 50, 75, and 100 watt range can be a useful heating supplement used in conjunction with heat pads. Large or gravid boa constrictors and anacondas benefit from a "very hot" spot. This can be an area of the enclosure where such a bulb is mounted above the substrate heat source. The spot bulb should be operating in conjunction with the daylight portion of the species' photoperiod.

Spotlight bulbs are an important source of heat for arboreal boas. Many arboreal species will not descend from branches to utilize substrate heat. For these species the appropriate wattage heat bulbs must be supplied. The bulb placement should be such as to allow for thermoregulation. One side of the enclosure can be fitted with a lighting fixture. Several branches should be provided throughout the enclosure with some angling upward under the heat bulb. With this arrangement the arboreal inhabitants can move across from branch to branch as well as vertically to warmer or cooler areas of the enclosure. Light bulbs should not be accessible to the inhabitants, as burns can occur. In some situations a loose covering of the bulb with hardware cloth may be the only needed precaution. Red light bulbs can be operated as a heat source at night without affecting photoperiod.

Any heating devices may be connected to automatic timers, which can limit their use during nighttime temperature drops.

Products for Precise Control of Heating Devices

An output limiting device is necessary where overheating is possible. One should be used with any of the above heating devices where a rheostat or dimmer switch is called for.

The dimmer box is solid state, has a 600 watt rating, and can be mounted in a convenient location. One or two heating devices can be plugged into the dual receptacle. As a knob is turned clockwise, the neon indicator light intensifies as power increases, and the heating device becomes warmer. Dimmer boxes are available with a 3 or 6 foot cord, and contain UL listed material. Larger units (1000 and 1500 watt) are also available.

The Microclimate thermostat is available in 260 watt and 500 watt maximum models. It is a proportional thermostat with a range of 18–33°C (64°–92°F). Microclimates can accurately maintain preset temperatures, as ambient temperature differentials do not affect operation. Many features are available on the deluxe model such as programmable nighttime drop, digital readouts, high and low recorded temperatures, indicator light, and an alarm. The remote sensor is useful when incorporated into an incubator.

These heating devices and their application to specific boa constrictor species will be referred to throughout this volume. Sources for these products are as follows:

Pipe heat tapes	Keith Wisner
Fiberglass heat pads	2947 Kenmore
Dimmer boxes	Berkley, MI 48072
	(313) 546-5287
Galvanized metal heat pads	The Herp House
	1750 Haines Road
	Orwell, OH 44076
	(216) 685-4615, FAX:
	(216) 685-4572
Microclimate thermostats	Bob Clark
Flex-watt heat tape	12316 Val Verde Drive
	Oklahoma City, OK 73142
	(405) 749-0797
Spotlight bulbs	Lighting dealers
Red light bulbs	Hardware stores

GENERAL HUSBANDRY CONSIDERATIONS

Healthy, well-established captive boas are a direct result of responsible husbandry practices. Proper husbandry is also the key to achieving successful captive boa reproduction.

Effective husbandry practices should revolve around a precise maintenance schedule. Enclosures should be serviced when soiled. Shed skins should be removed shortly after ecdysis. Water bowls and reusable substrate material should be scrubbed with a stiff bristle brush and antibacterial soap. A diluted chlorine bleach and water solution of 20:1 can then be used as a disinfectant. All items should be rinsed thoroughly to remove any traces of soap or bleach.

Any instruments used for enclosure maintenance should be disinfected after each use. The herpetoculturist's hands should be thoroughly washed with an antibacterial soap after *each* enclosure is serviced.

Record keeping is also an important aspect of captive boa husbandry. Events such as feeding, ecdysis, and defecation should be recorded for each specimen. Propagation data such as cycling dates and temperatures, dates of copulation and parturition, and litter size should also be recorded. Information such as age, sex, and the source from which the boa was obtained should be on record for each specimen.

When acquiring boas, captive-produced specimens are always the most desirable. Boas produced in captivity are free from the stress associated with capture and importation, and should be free of parasites. Captive-produced boas are also desirable from a conservation standpoint, as they are not contributing to the depletion of wild populations.

Quarantine procedures are rarely necessary for newly acquired captive boas obtained from reputable boa breeders who do not maintain wild-caught stock. Any wild-caught imported boa or boa acquired from an unknown source should be quarantined for a minimum of 30 days.

All newly acquired boas should be given a complete overall inspection. The nostrils, mouth, and throat should be examined for signs of respiratory illness and stomatitis. Indications of a problem can include gaping of the mouth, wheezing, or a discharge of mucus. Check for alertness, tongue flicking, and body movement abnormalities. Skin condition should be evaluated, as well as an inspection made for retained eye caps. The skin should not be dull, blistered, discolored, or excessively dry. Boas should have good body weight with no longitudinal skin folds. All newly acquired specimens should be inspected for the presence of snake mites (*Ophionyssus* sp.). Any boa which is not positively known to be captive-produced should have a fecal sample analyzed for the presence of endoparasites.

Housing

A variety of enclosures can be constructed or adapted to properly house boas. Wooden enclosures can be constructed by covering 2 × 2 inch framing with ½ or ¾ inch thickness exterior grade plywood. Holes must be cut or drilled to allow for sufficient ventilation. If the enclosure is used to house a female boa that is involved in a breeding project, the ventilation holes must be small enough to prevent the escape of any offspring which may be born in the enclosure. Large ventilation holes or openings should be covered with ⅛ to ¼ inch mesh hardware cloth, which can be stapled to the outside of the wooden enclosure.

Wooden enclosures can be sealed by applying a minimum of two to three coats of two part epoxy paint. In addition all corners and crevices where the framing meets the plywood can be caulked with a 100% silicone caulk. Always apply the caulk after the enclosure has been painted, as paint does not adhere well to silicone. A plexiglass panel can be installed in the front or end of a wooden enclosure. This will allow light to enter the enclosure, and provide a means for viewing the inhabitants.

The advantage of wooden enclosures is that they can be constructed to any size to meet specific requirements. Wooden enclosures can be designed as front or top opening to meet the needs of the herpetoculturist.

The disadvantages to wooden enclosures are that they are heavy and somewhat difficult to clean and disinfect.

Glass terraria have been used effectively for decades to house neonate boas, as well as boa species which do not attain a large size. The smaller sizes of glass terraria are the most useful when housing boas. This is primarily due to the availability of manufactured screen covers. Penn Plax Plastics, Inc. (Garden City, New York) produces high quality metal screen covers to fit glass terraria of 21–110 L (5½–29 gal) size. Two spring steel clips hold the screen cover securely to the terrarium. When the screen cover and clips are properly applied (the clips may require some compressing), the glass terrarium becomes nearly escape proof. I have had dozens of the Penn Plax screen covers in use over the last 10 years, without experiencing a single escape.

Opaque contact paper can be applied to the back and both end panels of all glass terraria to help provide a feeling of security for captive boas. This will also prevent boas from viewing the contents of neighboring enclosures, which is especially beneficial during feeding attempts. The contact paper should be applied to the outside surface of the terraria to prevent the paper from becoming soiled.

Glass terraria provide a clean, uniform appearance, and fit well on shelving due to their rectangular design. Glass terraria are also easy to disinfect.

The disadvantages to glass terraria are that they are relatively heavy and very breakable, and in addition the corners and underside of the plastic rim are difficult to clean when heavily soiled. Custom covers must be fabricated in order to maintain boas in large capacity glass terraria.

Vacuum-formed ABS plastic enclosures specifically designed to house reptiles are manufactured and distributed by Neodesha Plastics, Inc. (P.O. Box 371, Neodesha, KS (316) 325-3096). See Figure 5. Plastic reptile enclosures are available in a wide variety of styles and sizes, ranging from "the shoebox" which measures 30 × 16 × 8 cm (11.75 × 6.25 × 3.25 in), to the 96 inch model at 241 × 74 × 60 cm high (95 × 29 × 23½ in). Custom enclosures are also fabricated to meet individual herpetoculturists' needs.

The Neodesha plastics enclosures are ideal for housing all species of boas. See Figure 6. The enclosures are well constructed and nearly unbreakable, with rounded corners which offer easy cleaning. The opaque top, bottom, and sides provide a feeling of security for the boa. Although ventilation openings can be custom cut to meet specific boa keeper's needs, the standard ventilation design has proven to be beneficial for housing tropical boas, as high humidity levels can easily be achieved. Tempered glass or plexiglass slides within a top and bottom track to form a front opening enclosure. The glass front is slightly angled which allows for easy viewing of the inhabit-

Figure 5 Metal shelving containing Neodesha Plastics shoebox enclosures, which can accommodate neonate boas. Courtesy of Bill Fogel Photography.

Figure 6 Wooden shelves supporting Neodesha Plastics enclosures (primarily 36 inch models). Courtesy of Bill Fogel Photography.

ants. The Neodesha plastics enclosures are designed to nest within one another to save space during storage.

An optional "dam" or litter guard can be ordered for any of the various sizes of Neodesha plastic enclosures. The dam is a strip of plastic which is permanently adhered to the lower front edge of the enclosure. The dam will prevent substrate material from falling from the enclosure when opened. This is especially beneficial when housing sand boas (*Eryx*), for which a deep substrate for burrowing must be provided.

Neodesha manufactures metal rack units which can be used to maximize floor space by allowing plastic enclosures to be stacked three high.

Hide boxes should be incorporated into the majority of boa enclosures. The security provided by a small, opaque shelter can eliminate a great deal of stress for a captive boa. This can often be the difference between an acclimated boa and one which refuses food. A minimum of two hide boxes per enclosure is recommended—one on and one off the substrate heat source. This set-up allows the boa to thermoregulate without sacrificing the security of a hide box. Commercially manufactured hide boxes are easy to clean and disinfect, and are available in a variety of sizes. Shelters for large boas can be constructed by removing the lower portion from a section of plastic pipe.

Arboreal boas (*Corallus*) should be maintained in tall enclosures equipped with elevated, sturdy branches. Specialized housing requirements will be addressed per species later in this volume.

Water bowls containing clean water should be accessible to boas. The majority of boa species will benefit from bowls or tubs large enough for complete submersion. Soaking in a water container will often aid in the skin shedding process. Water bowls should be replaced with clean water once a week, or more frequently if soiled.

Boas should be housed individually. This will prevent two or more captive boas from trying to ingest the same food item (and possibly each other) during feeding attempts. If a health problem arises, the risk of infection transmitted from one boa to another is lessened by housing boas individually. Housing boas individually lessens the risk of a boa keeper being injured during feeding attempts or enclosure maintenance, especially by large boas. It is also beneficial to house sexually mature specimens separately, as the introduction of the opposite sex can stimulate breeding.

Substrate Material

The choice of substrate material is to a degree one of personal preference. However, various substrate materials possess inherent advantages or disadvantages when applied to captive boa husbandry. If public display is not a concern, the substrate should be one that most benefits the species being maintained while allowing for efficient servicing of the enclosure. The aesthetic value or naturalistic look of the substrate in this case is not of primary concern.

Astroturf is an excellent substrate for the majority of boa enclosures. Astroturf is extremely durable, easy to clean and disinfect, and aesthetically pleasing to most keepers. The coarse surface texture of astroturf provides excellent traction for boas, as well as aiding in the skin sloughing process.

When maintaining tropical boa species, high humidity can be easily achieved within a given enclosure by adding water to the astroturf and utilizing a heat pad or heat tape beneath the enclosure. This method is especially effective when used with plastic or glass terraria. Astroturf will absorb a large volume of water yet remain dry on the surface.

It is ideal to have two pieces of astroturf per enclosure. This will allow a clean piece of turf to replace the soiled piece without immediate washing. Several soiled pieces of astroturf can be cleaned together at a convenient time. The high quality double woven-backed astroturf should be used in boa enclosures. The lesser quality rubber-backed turf deteriorates over time. High quality astroturf can be found at carpet stores.

Astroturf is not recommended for large boa enclosures, as large pieces of turf are difficult to properly clean and disinfect. Astroturf should not be used with fossorial boas such as *Eryx*.

A substrate material suitable for burrowing should be used when housing fossorial boa species. Bird and Reptile Litter (Northeastern Products Corp., Warrensburg, NY) is highly recommended for this purpose. The litter consists of small natural dried wood chips, which are relatively dust free. The enclosure floor can be covered with any one of the three sizes of Bird and Reptile Litter chips to the appropriate depth (depending on the girth of the boa). This will provide fossorial species the opportunity to burrow beneath the substrate, providing a more natural, secure, and less stressful environment.

Litter material allows for more efficient cage maintenance when compared with a sand or soil substrate. Sand and soil are heavy and tend to adhere to the floor and walls of an enclosure. When used in glass terraria, sand and soil will adhere to silicone and become trapped under the plastic rim.

Wood bark chips can be used as a substrate to maintain many captive boa species. Bark chips are somewhat expensive and more labor intensive to replace than previously listed substrate material. Pine shavings, cypress mulch, and dried corn cob litter are not recommended as substrates for captive boa enclosures, as they produce excessive dust. The dust can lead to respiratory infections. The possibility of ingestion is also a hazard. Cedar shavings are known to be toxic to snakes and should not be used as a substrate material for boas.

Paper is the preferred substrate for large enclosures. Any absorbent, nonglossy type of paper will provide a decent substrate. A paper substrate is inexpensive, does not have to be cleaned, and is easily disposed. Paper will act as an insulator for a heating device below the floor of the enclosure. The number of layers of paper can be altered to allow the appropriate amount of heat to radiate through to the captive boa.

Food and Feeding

Boas are carnivores. Mammals, birds, other reptiles, amphibians, fish, and insects are consumed by boas in the wild.

It is relatively easy to meet the food requirements for the majority of captive boa species. Difficulty can be encountered when feeding neonate and juvenile boas which feed upon different prey than adults of the same species. For example, captive adult Haitian boas (*Epicrates striatus striatus*) will readily feed on mice and rats, while neonates show no interest in rodents, but will readily feed on small *Anolis* lizards. Certain smaller boa species naturally feed on specialized prey as adults, including small lizards, frogs, insects, or fish, and therefore can be difficult to feed in captivity.

There are several strategies which can entice a boa to feed upon a food item which it would normally reject. Huff (1977a) reports success using a scenting technique, which consists of grinding the body of an *Anolis* lizard to a pulp. After a small amount of water is added, newborn pink mice (pinkies) are dipped in the fluid and offered to neonate *Epicrates* which are not accepting unscented pinkies. As snakes greatly rely on their olfactory sense for determining prey suitability, it can be beneficial to first wash the pink mice with surgical soap, then thoroughly rinse with water prior to scenting. This can aid in removing the natural mouse odor. Another method which has proven successful in enticing reluctant neonate boas to feed on newborn pink mice is to split the head of the pinkie with a razor blade, exposing the brain. Funk (1981) reports that growth was accelerated in neonate Haitian boas after stuffing pre-killed *Anolis* lizards with cut-up pink mice, when compared to feeding just *Anolis* lizards. Some neonate boas prefer a fuzzy mouse (2–3 week old) or rat pink over a pink mouse for their first meal. In many cases it is a trial and error process before finding the right combination of factors which will entice a neonate boa to voluntarily accept the first meal. Once the first or second meal is accepted, the majority of neonate boas will not be problem feeders. Feeding neonate boas should not be attempted until after their first ecdysis.

Reluctant adult specimens may be induced to feed by heating the head of a prekilled rodent with a light bulb prior to placing the rodent in the boa enclosure. It is recommended that the heated head of the food item be placed just within the opening of an occupied hide box or shelter.

Specific feeding requirements will be addressed per species in the following chapters.

In the wild, many boas are opportunistic feeders, primarily employing a lie and wait approach. As boas are secretive by nature, many captive specimens will be more inclined to feed when provided with the necessary sense of security. Hide boxes or shelters have been discussed previously, in addition to substrate materials which can be burrowed beneath to provide a sense of security. In addition to fossorial species, neonate boas of nonfossorial species such as *Acrantophis dumerili* may benefit greatly from this type of substrate. This husbandry detail can oftentimes be the determining factor in persuading a neonate to accept its first meal.

Boas rely greatly on their sense of smell in addition to sight, and in certain species, heat-sensing labial pits aid in locating suitable prey. These are important factors to consider when maintaining captive boas. In captivity boas can associate movement (even shadows cast by room lighting) with feeding. Many boa keepers only open an enclosure when it is time to feed or service the enclosure. This can condition boas to expect food when the keeper is moving near the enclosure or manipulating it for any reason. The expectation of being fed is heightened when the odor of rodents is present within the room. It is often a worthwhile precaution to cover the front (and ends, if transparent) of an enclosure with cloth or paper after feeding, to prevent feeding strikes which could cause injury to the boa. Covering enclosures housing specimens that are not being fed may be necessary if rodents are present in the same room. I have observed caudal luring by *Boa constrictor* subspecies and *Acrantophis dumerili* when the boas observed movement within the room in which they were housed, even though no rodents (or food items) were present. In this condition it requires very little additional stimuli to elicit a feeding response (strike) from the boas.

The amount of food consumed by captive boas must be regulated. Many herpetoculturists feed neonate boids excessively, in hopes of growing them to reproductive size in a minimum amount of time. This process can produce boids with hugely obese bodies and alarmingly small heads, and ultimately shorten the life of the boid (Fogel, 1992). Huff (1980) states that attempting to grow a snake too fast during its youth may shorten its life span, and adversely affect its reproductive life. In addition Huff mentions that most captive snakes which he has observed are overweight. I have observed newly imported boids which were always considerably thinner than captive specimens of the same species or subspecies. These imports were only days out of the wild and had not been held in compounds. A good rule of thumb to follow when feeding captive boas is to feed neonates and juveniles an appropriate size meal every 6 or 7 days and adults every 7–14 days. See Figure 7. Digestion and elimination typically require 5–7 days. Digestion time is greatly influenced by the size of the meal consumed, as well as the body temperature of the boa.

It is important for captive boas which are designated as breeders to be well conditioned. Good body weight is especially important for breeder females, as they may refuse food during the gestation period. Good body weight does not mean obesity, and close attention should be paid to ensure that captive boas are not fed to the point of becoming obese. Although many male boas will refuse food during the breeding season, it is not as critical to maintain breeder males at a heavier body weight. The breeding season is relatively short and, unlike many female

Figure 7   A juvenile *Eryx colubrinus loveridgei* consuming a pink (approximately 1 week old mouse). Courtesy of Bill Fogel Photography.

Figure 8 A juvenile *Boa c. constrictor* constricting an adult mouse. Courtesy of Bill Fogel Photography.

boas, males will resume feeding following breeding. If males are allowed to become too heavy they can become sluggish and less willing to breed. It is difficult to determine a boa's ideal weight. An overly rounded "sausage shape" or unnatural scale separation are indications of obesity.

The decision whether to feed live or dead food animals to captive boas must be addressed. See Figure 8. When the food animals are small and present no danger to the captive boa (through biting or scratching), live prey can be offered to boas. When larger food animals such as adult mice, rats, guinea pigs, rabbits, etc. are required, it is wise to offer pre-killed prey. Even a food animal as small as an adult mouse has teeth large enough to puncture a boa's eye. It is not unusual for a captive

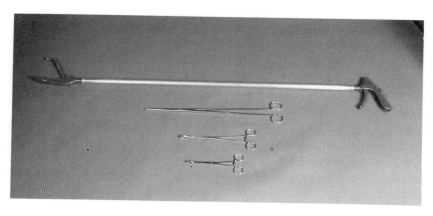

Figure 9 Tongs and forceps are an effective aid when feeding boas. Courtesy of Bill Fogel Photography.

boa to seize the rear portion of live prey, giving the prey the opportunity to turn and bite. Captive boas can be reluctant to accept pre-killed prey, but with patience and persistence most boas can be enticed to feed.

Pre-killed food animals can be presented to captive boas with the aid of forceps or tongs. See Figure 9. Live prey movement can be simulated when introducing a pre-killed food item into the enclosure. After the prey is seized by the boa, slight resistance can be applied to the prey via the forceps during the constriction process. This can aid in preventing the boa from rejecting the pre-killed prey. Boas may prefer freshly killed food items over those previously frozen and thawed, as the scents may differ. The forceps and tongs should be disinfected between feedings.

It can be beneficial to feed juvenile boas both small rats and mice, rather than just mice. I have observed a boa which was fed only mice for the first 2 years, and it seemed to become "imprinted" on this food item. As a 2 m (6 ft) adult, it still greedily feeds upon mice, but is extremely reluctant to accept a rat. It is neither cost effective nor efficient to feed many mice instead of a single rat. Chicks or an appropriately sized chicken can be offered to some captive boa species once a month or so as a dietary supplement.

When boas are due to shed and their eyes become opaque ("blue"), feeding should be postponed until after ecdysis.

Vitamin supplements are not thought to be necessary for captive boa health or development. As boas are consuming whole food animals, all necessary nutrients should be derived from the food animal. I have used Linatone as a vitamin supplement for captive boas by adding a few drops to a food item, but have noticed no discernible benefits.

Many captive boas have lived in excess of 20 years. A *Boa constrictor constrictor* lived 40 years, 4 months, and 15 days in captivity (Snider and Bowler, 1992).

C1. An adult female common boa constrictor (*Boa c. constrictor*) consuming a rat. Courtesy of Bill Fogel Photography.

C2. A Bolivian red-tail boa (*Boa constrictor amarali*). Courtesy of Al Baldogo.

PLATE 1

C3. A red-tail boa (*Boa constrictor* subsp.) which was captured in Pucallpa, Peru. Courtesy of Carl May.

PLATE 2

C4. A subadult red-tail boa (*Boa constrictor* subsp.) exhibiting characteristics which herpeteculturists have associated with the Surinam red-tail boa. Photo by author.

C5. The Argentine boa (*Boa constrictor occidentalis*) has become common in captive collections. Courtesy of Al Baldogo.

PLATE 3

C6. The clouded boa (*Boa constrictor nebulosus*). Courtesy of John H. Tashjian and Vince Scheidt.

C7. The Hogg Island boa (*Boa constrictor* subsp.) has the ability to change color and has become popular among herpetoculturists. Courtesy of Al Baldogo.

PLATE 4

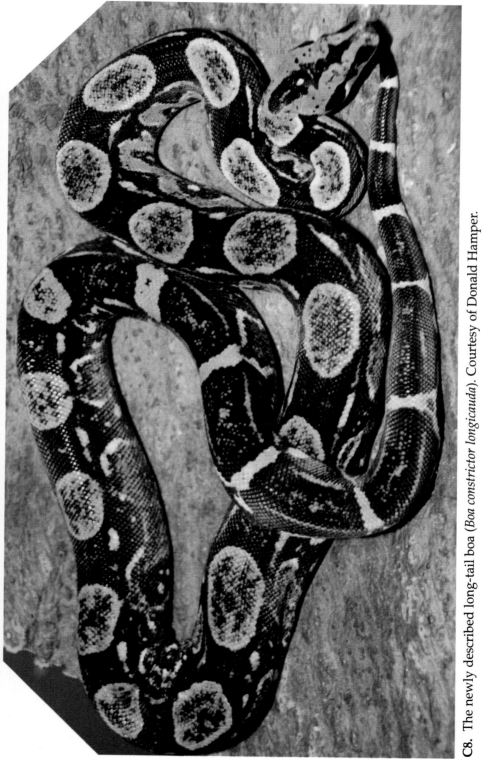

C8. The newly described long-tail boa (*Boa constrictor longicauda*). Courtesy of Donald Hamper.

PLATE 5

C9. An adult female Brazilian rainbow boa (*Epicrates c. cenchria*). Considered to be the most attractive of the rainbow boa complex. Courtesy of Bill Fogel Photography.

C10. A female *Epicrates c. cenchria*, with her neonates still encased in their fetal membranes. Courtesy of Dick Goergen.

PLATE 6

C11. An adult female Colombian rainbow boa (*Epicrates cenchria maurus*). Courtesy of Bill Fogel Photography.

C12. An adult Argentine rainbow boa (*Epicrates cenchria alvarezi*). Courtesy of Bill Fogel Photography.

PLATE 7

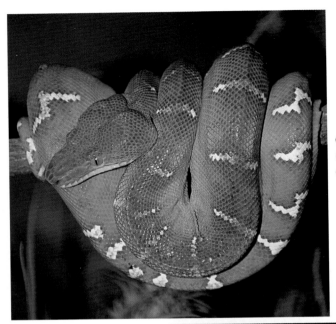

C13. The emerald tree boa (*Corallus caninus*). Courtesy of Peter J. Stafford.

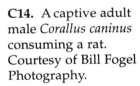

C14. A captive adult male *Corallus caninus* consuming a rat. Courtesy of Bill Fogel Photography.

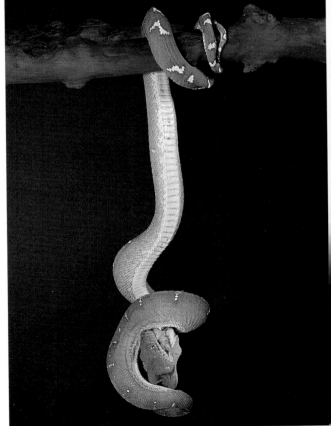

PLATE 8

C15. A pair of copulating *Corallus caninus.* Courtesy of Dick Goergen.

C16. A female *Corallus caninus* giving birth. Courtesy of Dick Goergen.

PLATE 9

C17. A juvenile *Corallus caninus* of the red color phase. Courtesy of Peter J. Stafford.

C18. An adult male Amazon tree boa (*Corallus e. enydris*). Courtesy of Stephen Chandler.

PLATE 10

C19. The Cook's tree boa (*Corallus enydris cooki*). Courtesy of Robert W. Henderson.

C20. The annulated boa (*Corallus annulatus*) is highly variable in color and pattern. Courtesy of John H. Tashjian and Fort Worth Zoo.

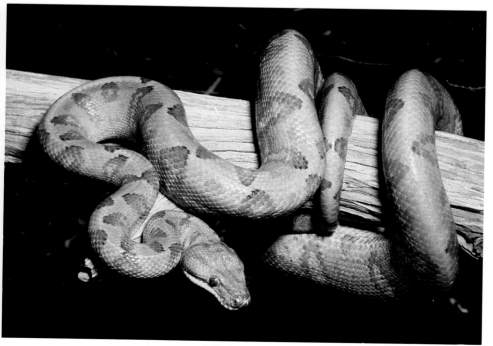

PLATE 11

C21. *Corallus annulatus.* Courtesy of John H. Tashjian and Fort Worth Zoo.

PLATE 12

C22. The Cuban boa (*Epicrates angulifer*) is a protected species. Courtesy of Al Baldogo.

C23. A juvenile *Epicrates angulifer.* Courtesy of Al Baldogo.

PLATE 13

C24. The Virgin Islands boa (*Epicrates monensis granti*). Courtesy of John H. Tashjian and San Antonio Zoo.

C25. An adult male Jamaican boa (*Epicrates subflavus*). Courtesy of Bill Fogel Photography.

PLATE 14

C26. The Turk's Island boa (*Epicrates c. chrysogaster*).
Courtesy of Kevin and Sue Hanley ©.

C27. An adult male Haitian boa (*Epicrates s. striatus*).
Courtesy of Stephen Chandler.

PLATE 15

C28. A Berry Island boa (*Epicrates striatus fowleri*). Courtesy of Al Baldogo.

C29. A juvenile green anaconda (*Eunectes murinus*). Photo by author.

PLATE 16

C30. A juvenile yellow anaconda (*Eunectes notaeus*).
Courtesy of Stephen Chandler.

C31. The Little Cayman dwarf boa (*Tropidophis caymanensis parkeri*).
Courtesy of John H. Tashjian and Dallas Zoo.

PLATE 17

C32. The Western Cuba banded dwarf boa (*Tropidophis feicki*).
Courtesy of John H. Tashjian and Reptilien Haus.

C33. *Tropidophis haetianus.* Courtesy of Kevin and Sue Hanley ©.

PLATE 18

C34. The Northern eyelash boa (*Trachyboa boulengeri*) is rare in captive collections. Courtesy of John H. Tashjian and Houston Zoo.

C35. *Trachyboa boulengeri*. Note the distinctive nasal and supraorbital horns. Courtesy of John H. Tashjian and San Antonio Zoo.

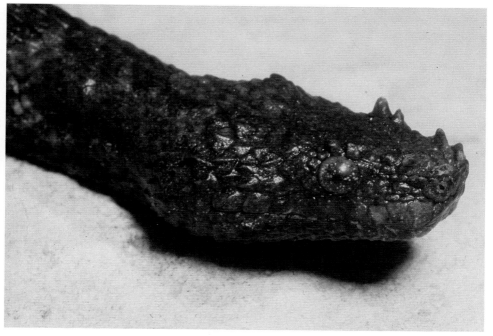

PLATE 19

C36. The Southern eyelash boa (*Trachyboa gularis*). Courtesy of John H. Tashjian and San Antonio Zoo.

C37. The Chipan boa (*Ungaliophis continentalis*). Courtesy of John H. Tashjian and Dallas Zoo.

PLATE 20

C38. A male
Panamanian dwarf boa
(*Ungaliophis panamensis*). Courtesy of John H. Tashjian and Houston Zoo.

C39. The Oaxacan dwarf boa (*Exiliboa placata*) inhabits cool montane cloud
forests. Courtesy of John H. Tashjian and Fort Worth Zoo.

PLATE 21

C40. The Kenyan sand boa (*Eryx colubrinus loveridgei*) is common in captive collections, and frequently reproduced. Courtesy of Bill Fogel Photography.

C41. An adult anerythristic *Eryx colubrinus loveridgei*. This mutation lacks red pigment and is being produced in captivity.
Courtesy of Stephen Hammack of H.I.S.S.

PLATE 22

C42. An amelanistic *Eryx colubrinus loveridgei,* lacking black pigment. Courtesy of Donald Hamper.

C43. A gravid female rough-scaled sand boa (*Eryx conicus*) on a Bird and Reptile Litter substrate. Courtesy of Bill Fogel Photography.

PLATE 23

C44. An adult male *Eryx conicus.* Courtesy of Bill Fogel Photography.

C45. A juvenile Dumeril's boa (*Acrantophis dumerili*). Courtesy of Bill Fogel Photography.

PLATE 24

C46. An adult male *Acrantophis dumerili*. Head scalation differs between the two *Acrantophis* species. Courtesy of Bill Fogel Photography.

C47. A neonate Madagascar ground boa (*Acrantophis madagascariensis*). This species typically produces a small number of extremely large neonates. Courtesy of Sean McKeown.

PLATE 25

C48. A juvenile *Acrantophis madagascariensis.* Very few births have been recorded in captivity. Courtesy of Sean McKeown.

C49. A juvenile *Acrantophis madagascariensis.* Courtesy of Sean McKeown.

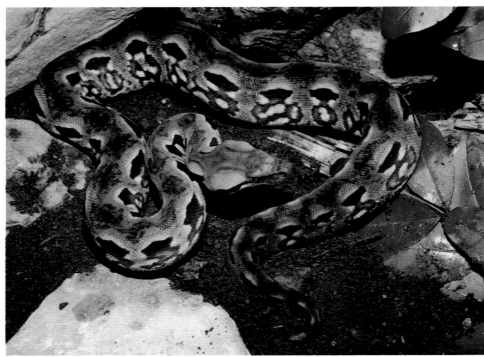

PLATE 26

C50. The Madagascar tree boa (*Sanzinia madagascariensis*) is a semi-arboreal species. Courtesy of Peter J. Stafford.

C51. *Sanzinia madagascariensis.* Courtesy of Kevin and Sue Hanley ©.

PLATE 27

C52. A juvenile *Sanzinia madagascariensis* exhibiting red/orange coloration. Courtesy of Kevin and

PLATE 28

C53. The Round Island boa (*Casarea dussumieri*) has only been captively reproduced at Jersey Wildlife Preservation Trust. Courtesy of John H. Tashjian and Jersey Wildlife Preservation Trust.

C54. The Pacific ground boa. (*Candoia c. carinata*).
Courtesy of Kevin and Sue Hanley ©.

PLATE 29

C55. *Candoia carinata.* Courtesy of Peter J. Stafford.

C56. The New Guinea viper boa (*Candoia aspera*).
Courtesy of Kevin and Sue Hanley ©.

PLATE 30

C57. The Solomon Islands tree boa (*Candoia bibroni australis*).
Courtesy of Kevin and Sue Hanley ©.

C58. A juvenile Mexican rosy boa (*Lichanura t. trivirgata*).
Courtesy of Stephen Chandler.

PLATE 31

C59. An adult desert rosy boa (*Lichanura trivirgata roseofusca*) on an astroturf substrate. Photo by author.

C60. A juvenile Pacific rubber boa (*Charina b. bottae*). Juvenile rubber boas are considerably lighter in coloration than adults. Courtesy of Sean McKeown.

PLATE 32

SECTION 3
PROPAGATION

BOA REPRODUCTION

In the wild, the majority of tropical boas have a specific season in which breeding occurs. The breeding season can be triggered by environmental cues such as temperature or photoperiod fluctuations, or the onset of the rainy season.

Captive boas can be induced to breed by manipulating environmental factors. Although tropical boas occur in a wide variety of habitats and geographic localities, there are common factors which can be manipulated to induce successful reproduction.

It is important to accurately determine the sex of captive boas when the objective is to achieve successful reproduction. Many boa species do display some degree of sexual dimorphism. Female boas attain a larger size, and males possess a relatively longer tail and usually develop anal spurs.

Mechanical probing is the suggested method of determining the sex of boas. The sexing probe is a long thin rod with rounded ends. See Figure 10. Some probes are flexible and may have probing tips on either end. Sexing probes are available in a variety of sizes, and the proper diameter probe tip should be carefully determined based on the size of the individual boa. The probe should be thoroughly wiped with an alcohol prep pad prior to and after each probing procedure. The sexing probe should be lubricated prior to the actual probing procedure. I prefer mineral oil as a probing lubricant over any of the jelly type lubricants. Mineral oil is thin, very slippery, and safe enough for human consumption. Certain jelly type lubricants can act as a spermicide, and therefore may interfere with breeding.

During the probing procedure, the sexing probe is inserted caudally into the cloacal opening. See Figure 11. The probe

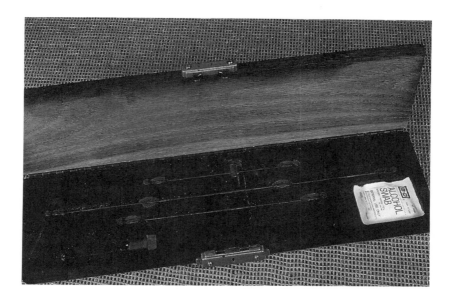

Figure 10 A set of sexing probes, boxed with a vial of mineral oil and alcohol prep pads. Courtesy of Bill Fogel Photography.

should be guided to either the near or far side of the vent. The probe should not be directed down the center of the tail. The depth to which the probe reaches when slight resistance is felt is measured by counting the number of subcaudal scales. See Figure 12. By comparing the withdrawn probe against the subcaudal scales a count can be taken, and sex determined. See Figure 13. As a rule of thumb the probe will typically pass up to a depth of only three subcaudals when probing a female specimen. A male specimen will typically accept the probe to a depth of at least eight to sixteen subcaudals. For species specific probing depth information, Table 1 should be consulted.

A seminal plug is comprised of dried semen that adheres to the hemipenes of a male snake. Mengden et al. (1980) noted that the presence of a seminal plug could cause an obstruction when probing. Laszlo (1975) reports the Madagascan boas (*Acrantophis* and *Sanzinia*) as being difficult to sex by mechanical probing.

Sexual maturity for a normally fed and maintained boa is

typically reached in 3–5 years. Sexually immature animals will not successfully breed. Male boas usually reach sexual maturity at a smaller size and slightly younger age than females. Sexually mature boas can exhibit signs of restlessness by prowling within their enclosure, often with the tail raised. This behavior usually takes place after temperature cycling and the introduction of the opposite sex.

Groups of sexually mature boas may have higher reproductive success than one pair of breeders. The use of multiple males per single female greatly increases the chances of successful captive reproduction, as a given male might not impregnate a given female. Multiple males can also be beneficial in stimulating breeding through male-male combat. Breeding attempts can certainly be made when only a single sexual pair is available. I have noted copulation among *Boa constrictor constrictor*, *Epicrates cenchria maurus*, *Epicrates subflavus*, and *Eryx conicus*, while maintaining only a single male and female of each. All of the above copulations were successful and produced young.

There is no set formula or "recipe" which can guarantee reproductive success for tropical boas. In order for successful reproduction to occur, male boas must produce viable sperm, and female boas must successfully ovulate prior to copulation. The major factors which can be manipulated in order for captive tropical boas to reproduce are temperature, humidity, and photoperiod.

It is commonly accepted that temperature manipulation (cycling) is the single most important factor in captive boa reproduction. Huff (1979) believes that in some cases seasonal temperature changes are probably totally responsible for the inducement of mating in snakes. The most widely employed method of temperature cycling consists of gradually reducing the ambient temperature for an appropriate period of time and raising the temperature to induce successful captive reproduction. It is important to research the climate of the geographic region in which the boa species naturally occurs to determine the cycling temperatures. Temperatures should remain warm enough to avoid respiratory ailments. Tropical boas do not hibernate in the wild and must not be hibernated in captivity.

Unlike species which occur in temperature regions, captive

Figure 11   After cleaning with alcohol and lubricating with mineral oil, the sexing probe is inserted into the cloacal opening. Courtesy of Bill Fogel Photography.

Figure 12   The thumb or thumbnail marks the exposed part of the probe nearest the vent, after slight resistance is felt. Courtesy of Bill Fogel Photography.

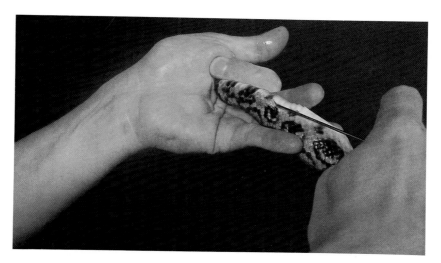

Figure 11 After cleaning with alcohol and lubricating with mineral oil, the sexing probe is inserted into the cloacal opening. Courtesy of Bill Fogel Photography.

Figure 12 The thumb or thumbnail marks the exposed part of the probe nearest the vent, after slight resistance is felt. Courtesy of Bill Fogel Photography.

Figure 13 Without moving the thumb from its mark, the probe is withdrawn and placed along the snake's tail. The number of sub-caudal scales is counted. This specimen is a female, as penetration was only three scales. Courtesy of Bill Fogel Photography.

Figure 13 Without moving the thumb from its mark, the probe is withdrawn and placed along the snake's tail. The number of subcaudal scales is counted. This specimen is a female, as penetration was only three scales. Courtesy of Bill Fogel Photography.

boas from warmer climates should not be exposed to cool temperatures for extended periods of time. Temperature cycling for tropical and warm climate boas can consist of determining a breeding season, and lowering the ambient temperature by 2°C (5°F) every 3 or 4 days until the desired low temperature is achieved. Supplemental heating devices should be discontinued during the cycling period. One method of cycling is to maintain the desired low temperature for a period of 4–8 weeks. An alternative method is to reach the desired low temperature only at night and restore the normal higher temperature during the day. A combination of these two methods can also be employed. The desired low temperature can be maintained for several weeks, followed by restoring higher temperatures during the day, while lowering the temperatures at night. I have had the most success by employing the latter (combination) method.

TABLE 1 Sex Determination by Probe Depth.
Ross and Marzec, 1990. With permission.

Taxonomic Identification	Number of Subcaudal Scales	
	Male	Female
Acrantophis dumerili	12	4
Acrantophis madagas-cariensis	10–12	4–5
Boa constrictor amarali	9	3–4
Boa constrictor constrictor	10–12	2–3
Boa constrictor imperator	10	3–4
Boa constrictor occidentalis	10–11	3
Boa constrictor orophias	10–12	2–4
Boa constrictor ortoni	10–12	4
Candoia aspera	9–10	2–3
Candoia bibroni australis	9–10	4
Candoia bibroni bibroni	9–10	4
Candoia carinata carinata	10–14	3
Candoia carinata paulsoni	10–12	3–4
Casarea dussumieri	15+	0
Charina bottae	15	3–5
Corallus annulatus	10–12	3
Corallus caninus	14–15	3
Corallus enydris cooki	11–14	3
Epicrates angulifer	9	3
Epicrates cenchria alvarezi	11	3–4
Epicrates cenchria cenchria	11	3
Epicrates cenchria maurus	7–9	2–3
Epicrates chrysogaster	8–9	2–3
Epicrates exsul	9	3
Epicrates fordi	8–9	2–3
Epicrates gracilis	8–9	2–3
Epicrates inornatus	8–9	2–3
Epicrates monensis	9	2–3
Epicrates striatus	9	2–3
Epicrates subflavus	9	3
Eryx colubrinus colubrinus	10–12	2–3
Eryx colubrinus loveridgei	10–12	2–3
Eryx jaculus	9	3
Eryx johni johni	6–9	2–4
Eryx johni persicus	7–9	3
Eryx tataricus	9	3–4

TABLE 1 Continued

Taxonomic Identification	Number of Subcaudal Scales	
	Male	Female
Eunectes murinus	19	2–3
Eunectes notaeus		2–3
Lichanura trivirgata	10	3
Sanzinia madagascariensis	8–10	3
Trachyboa gularis	9	3
Tropidophis	10	3
Ungaliophis		2

Just how low cycling temperatures should be allowed to fall, and for what period of time, can vary from one boa species to the next. The majority of tropical and warm climate boa species can "cycle in" at 21°C (70°F). Cycling is typically initiated November through January in North America. Respiratory illness can occur if captive tropical boas are subjected to temperatures below this for too long a period of time. Retes (1992) reports cycling *Acrantophis dumerili* at 4°C (40°F), and observing copulation at 7°C (45°F), with no problems. The author cautions against these temperature extremes. *Acrantophis dumerili* will copulate and produce viable young when provided with cycling temperature lows that are 15°C above the previously described temperatures. It is better to miss a year of viable offspring and have healthy adult boa breeding stock than to treat the breeders for a respiratory ailment. There is always an opportunity to adjust the cycling approach the following year.

Food should not be offered to boas for at least 2 weeks prior to temperature cycling, and boas should not be fed during cycling.

Humidity can play a role in captive boa reproduction. In the wild, breeding of some species is triggered by the rainy season. Huff (1984) reports maintaining *Acrantophis dumerili* at a relative humidity of 50–60% (somewhat higher in the summer), and misting the enclosure with tepid water to stimulate copulation. Mating can be stimulated in some boid species by spraying them with water chilled to 4–10°C (39–50°F). It is believed that the mating is stimulated more by the drop in temperature than by the increased humidity (Laszlo, 1984).

It is difficult to determine what effect photoperiod plays in captive boa reproduction. Wells (1980) states that successful captive reproduction in *Boa constrictor constrictor* was achieved with the female experiencing 24 hours of subdued light per day for 12 months, beginning prior to and continuing through gestation. No adverse effects on reproduction were observed. Walsh (1994) reports that photoperiod manipulation was not employed, and that a set photoperiod was not thought to be a contributing factor for the successful reproduction of captive *Corallus caninus* or *Epicrates cenchria cenchria*. Chiras (1979) reports that the photoperiod was not varied (enclosures were light from 0600–1800 hrs) throughout the year, yet he achieved considerable captive reproductive success with red-tail boas. Tolson and Henderson (1993) state that the alteration of photoperiod had no effect on plasma testosterone levels in male *Epicrates striatus*. My experience has shown that for several species of *Boa, Epicrates,* and *Eryx,* photoperiod did not play a significant role in captive reproduction. Specimens were exposed to very erratic photoperiods (often consisting of 17–18 hours of light per day), and reproduced as well as when exposed to a more traditional 12 light, 12 dark routine.

Boas should be maintained in separate enclosures. If adult breeders must be housed together, males should be housed separately from females, as the introduction of the opposite sexes to one another can act as a breeding stimulus. A separate enclosure designated for breeding purposes can be used. This is typically a larger enclosure than those housing the individual males or females. Males may be placed together prior to the introduction of the female. This can stimulate breeding behavior in some boa species through male-male combat. Male combat can consist of biting, constricting and trying to pin one another to the substrate.

Adult males and females can be introduced to one another for breeding purposes at the beginning of the cycling period or after cycling, when warmer temperatures are restored. I have achieved breeding success among various boa species by employing both methods. I prefer to introduce males into the females' enclosures. In the wild many male boids typically travel to seek out females during the breeding season. Chiras (1979) reports that when a female red-tail boa was introduced into a male's enclosure, the male experienced difficulty in courting her because the female explored the new enclosure and ignored his efforts. The reverse procedure proved to be more success-ful. Many boid breeders employ the opposite method by intro-ducing the females into the male's enclosure.

Placing shed boa skins in the breeding enclosure can act as a stimulus. Laszlo (1979) states that a shed skin from a female snake can be moistened and rubbed on her back to stimulate male snakes and induce mating. Huff (1979) reports that the accumulation of fecal matter, shed skins, and musk appears to stimulate *Epicrates* to copulate. Huff (1977b) mentions height-ened interest in copulation among captive *Epicrates* species after they were placed in cloth bags and driven in a car. Separation of the males and females from the breeding enclosure and reintro-duction after a few days can stimulate a breeding response.

Courtship among captive boas can consist of several behav-iors, but is easily recognizable. Gillingham et al. (1977) described breeding behaviors in snakes as consisting of four distinct phases: tactile-chase, tail-search copulatory attempt, tactile-alignment, and intromission. These phases can be recognized when observing captive boa courtship and breeding. Tactile-chase consists of prospective mate identification, with the male typically crawling alongside the female. Tongue flicking is usu-ally exhibited, and the male may demonstrate jerky movements, as well as stroking the female with his spurs. During tail-search copulatory attempt, the male rotates his tail beneath that of the female to align their cloacae. During tactile-alignment, the male aligns his cloaca with that of the female. Intromission consists of the male inserting one hemipenis into the female's cloaca.

The majority of wild boas are biennial breeders (every 2 years); however, in captivity where conditions such as food intake, tem-perature, etc. can be favorably adjusted, many boa species will produce offspring annually. Even under ideal conditions, some captive boa specimens produce young only biennially, even though copulation may occur annually. Biennial cycles are thought to be a natural phenomenon, possibly allowing females to recuperate from a lengthy gestation period and attain good physical condition for the next reproductive cycle. Female boas may refuse food during the gestation period, which can be in excess of 6 months. Walsh (1994) states that annual breeding of *Corallus caninus,* and *Epicrates c. cenchria* resulted in reduced fecundity, prolapsed cloaca, reduced muscle tone, and possibly premature death.

Determining when a female boa is gravid is fairly easy in most species. A noticeable swelling accompanied by scale separation is typically evident in the posterior third of the female's body. This appearance can be difficult to detect in a large, heavy-bodied *Boa constrictor* or anaconda. Having observed definite copulation during the breeding season is a good indicator that the female may be gravid. Gravid females may refuse food and seek out hot areas of the enclosure.

Even though copulation is positively observed, it is difficult to determine which copulation is responsible for fertilization. I maintained a female *Boa c. constrictor* which last copulated early January. Parturition occurred September 14 (a gestation period of 8–9 months). In the past this specimen's gestation period had never exceeded 6 months. It is believed that boas have the ability to store sperm.

It is important to provide additional heat for captive female boas which may be gravid. If female boas are not provided with adequate temperatures during the gestation period, deformed or dead offspring may be produced. Walsh (1994) observed that, when given a choice, gravid boas preferred warm temperatures that averaged 31 °C (88°F) for the majority of the gestation period. Temperatures that averaged 28°C (82°F) were preferred during the final few weeks prior to parturition. The gravid female should be observed for temperature preference. The enclosure which houses the female should provide a thermal gradient. If the female is constantly in the warmest area of the enclosure, this indicates that additional heat should be provided. If the female is constantly trying to avoid heat sources, this indicates that a cooler area should be provided.

Gravid boas typically become restless as they near parturition. Gravid females should be provided with a nest box containing a few inches of damp sphagnum moss. The nest box

Figure 14 An adult female *Epicrates c. cenchria* consuming a recently passed infertile ova (slug). Courtesy of Dick Goergen.

can consist of a plastic tub with low sides, and a cover to block the light.

Neonate boas should be removed from the female's enclosure as soon as possible. A large female can crush neonates by crawling over them or resting on them. In rare instances the female may consume her young. Huff (1980) reports a female *Epicrates s. striatus* giving birth to 21 young, four of which were stillborn. The female consumed the dead neonates and proceeded to consume a live neonate. A female *Epicrates exsul* attempted to consume her living offspring after consuming infertile ova and two stillborn young (Tolson, 1989).

There are reports of female boas consuming infertile ova ("slugs") and stillborn young, and ignoring live offspring. A litter of 14 *Eunectes notaeus* (six live and eight stillborn) was caged with the post-parturient female for a few hours. The female prodded the stillborn neonates with her snout and then ingested them, while ignoring the live neonates (Townson, 1985). Similar behavior has been observed in *Eunectes murinus* by Neill and Allen (1962). I have observed female *Epicrates subflavus*, and *Epicrates cenchria alvarezi* consuming recently passed infertile ova. Goergen (pers. comm.) has observed similar behavior in *Epicrates c. cenchria*. See Figure 14. By consuming the infertile ova the female may be replenishing nutrients lost during gestation. Groves (1980) suggested that this behavior may have survival benefits by eliminating the odors that are produced by birth debris which could attract predators.

Care should be exercised when removing neonates from the female's enclosure, as female boas may become aggressive after parturition.

SECTION 4
SPECIES ACCOUNTS

CENTRAL AND SOUTH AMERICAN BOAS

Boa constrictor constrictor and *Boa constrictor* Subspecies

This account will concentrate primarily on the common Colombian boa constrictor (*Boa constrictor constrictor*) as it is the most commonly maintained in captivity. *Boa c. constrictor* occurs in eastern Ecuador, northern and eastern Peru, northern Bolivia, Brazil north of about 13° S., central and eastern Colombia, Venezuela, the Guianas, and Trinidad and Tobago (Stimson, 1969).

There is much controversy as to the subspecific designations of the so-called red-tail boas. The pet trade adds to the confusion by designating geographic variants for red-tailed boas, such as Surinam and Guyanan red-tail boas. The problem with this is that there are no accepted taxonomic guidelines corresponding to these common names. A Surinam red-tail boa from one breeder may look completely different from a Surinam red-tail boa from another breeder. It is important to keep in mind that boa constrictors are highly variable in color and pattern and breeders generally do not possess exact locality data for their adult specimens. In the wild, localities overlap where interbreeding among the *Boa constrictor* subspecies and geographic variants occur. Many times boa constrictors are transported from the country of origin to neighboring countries for shipping to comply with exportation legalities.

To add to the confusion a recent trend for some breeders, dealers, and many pet shops is to label the common Colombian *Boa constrictor (Boa c. constrictor)* as a "Colombian red-tail boa." Although de Vosjoli (1990) mentions *Boa constrictor constrictor* as

45

a very rare Colombian red-tail boa out of the Amazon basin and llanos of Colombia (as well as Brazilian, Guyanan, and Surinam red-tail boas), there are no data in the literature to substantiate this claim. As *Boa constrictor constrictor* is the nominate form, it stands to reason that *Boa c. constrictor* is very common and certainly not a rare red-tail boa. They are not true red-tail boas, even though the more attractive specimens do sport a red and white coloration on their tails. *Boa constrictor amarali* and *Boa constrictor ortoni* are the only described true red-tail boa subspecies. I believe that Surinam and Guyanan "red-tails" should be considered true red-tail boas that are a separate subspecies, but one that is yet to be described. The true red-tail boas possess characteristics which differentiate them from other boa constrictors. The amount or intensity of the red coloration which appears on the tail is not necessarily the determining factor. The true red-tail boas usually have a long, narrow head, and dorsal markings which herpetoculturists refer to as "widow's peaks." These are small saddles with pointed, tapering, median projections both anteriorly and posteriorly. Although highly variable, red-tail boas typically possess an attractive ground color, which can be varying shades of pink and purple, as opposed to the primarily tan color of common boas.

Another alarming trend the pet trade has adopted is referring to wild-collected and imported herps as "farm bred." The reasoning is that, prior to exportation, the herps were produced (bred and born) on a herp farm. In reality this is far from the truth. The so-called farms are often nothing more than compounds or holding facilities located in the reptile's or amphibian's country of origin. In the case of common boas, the compounds are located in Colombia. After breeding season, gravid wild common *Boa constrictor* are collected and held in these compounds until giving birth. The females are then released or butchered for the skin trade, as they are not suitable for the pet trade. The neonate boas are held under inadequate conditions until there are sufficient numbers to fill overseas orders. The baby boas are then shipped to jobbers and wholesalers around the world, who in turn sell them to pet shops. This is the same procedure that has been used for decades, before the "farm-raised" concept became fashionable. The "farms" do not possess breeding facilities or captive-maintained breeding animals. The pet shops are still receiving nothing more than wild-caught imported (cheap) baby *Boa constrictor*. Tens of thousands of these baby boas exported from Colombia enter the United States annually. There is no substitute for the quality and health of captive-bred and born herps. Do the necessary research to know exactly what you are purchasing.

When considering *Boa constrictor* for captive maintenance, potential size must be taken into account. Although not one of the true giant snakes, female *Boa constrictor* subspecies can attain lengths of 3.75 m (12 ft). *Boa constrictor* subspecies are also heavy-bodied, powerful constrictors with large heads and large teeth. As with any large constrictor, care must be exercised when handling or feeding adult boas.

Neonate *Boa constrictor* can be housed in shoebox or sweater-box enclosures as well as ten gallon terraria. Large enclosures are required for adult boas. Plastic enclosures such as those manufactured by Neodesha Plastics are ideal. The majority of adult male *Boa constrictor* subspecies can be comfortably housed in the 48 inch model Neodesha enclosure; large females require the 72 or 96 inch models. I recommend housing boas individually, as this allows for safer maintenance and feeding, both for the snakes and the keeper.

An astroturf substrate works well for small (neonate to 1.2 m (4 ft long) boas. When larger enclosures are required for adult boas, astroturf becomes too difficult to properly clean to be practical. Paper or bark chips can be effectively used as a substrate for large boa enclosures.

Ambient temperature between 25°–29°C (78°–85°F) are ideal for *Boa c. constrictor*. The boa enclosure should be equipped with supplemental substrate heat in the form of a heat pad located at one end of the enclosure, providing a warm spot of 31–34.5°C (90–95°F). The warm spot should be large enough for the boa's entire body to rest upon, but should not cover more than one-half of the enclosure floor. It is important that boas be allowed to thermoregulate by moving on or off the heated floor area as needed.

As with other tropical herps, high humidity must be provided for *Boa constrictor* subspecies. A 75% relative humidity should be provided at all times to avoid shedding and respiratory problems. A shallow water container half filled with clean water should always be accessible. The container should be large enough to allow the boa to soak. Large plastic tubs which can be easily entered and are heavy enough not to be tipped work well for adult boas.

With the majority of *Boa constrictor* subspecies, sexual maturity is achieved between 3.5 and 5 years of age. *Boa c. constrictor* typically breed from September through February (Ross and Marzec, 1990), with December and January being the months with the most copulations observed.

Most breeders subject their *Boa constrictor* to a temperature cycling period in late fall or early winter. It is important to note that subjecting boas to temperatures that are too cool can lead to serious respiratory problems. If copulation has been observed, a heat lamp should be incorporated into the female *Boa constrictor* enclosure. The lamp should be suspended above the heated end of the enclosure to provide an extra hot spot of 37–40°C (100–105°F). This hot spot will be utilized by gravid females to aid in the development of the young. When additional heat is not provided, the risk of female boas producing infertile ova (slugs), stillborn young, or young with congenital defects is quite high.

Ross and Marzec (1990) state that *Boa constrictor* gestation usually ranges from 4–8 months with a record of 10 months. It has been my experience that female *Boa c. constrictor* continue to feed despite being gravid. During this period, I reduce the size of the food animal, and feed at no more than 3 week invervals. Other breeders have observed that female *Boa constrictor* will refuse food throughout the entire gestation period. It is important for the female boa to have adequate body weight and be completely healthy before breeding is attempted.

Goergen (pers. comm.) has observed parturition in late April and mid-June. I have observed the majority of parturition dates in late April and early May. Litters of as many as 60 young can be produced by a large female *Boa c. constrictor*. I have witnessed a litter of 52 viable young and two infertile ova (slugs) from a common Colombian boa constrictor.

Neonate *Boa c. constrictor* can be offered a "fuzzy" to "hopper"-

sized (2–3 week old) mouse after their first shed. The majority of baby *Boa constrictor* subspecies are very aggressive feeders. Neonate boas should be fed at 7–10 day intervals. Adults can be fed an appropriate-sized food item at 2 week intervals. Prekilled rodents are recommended to avoid possible injury to the snake.

The Mexican or Central American boa constrictor (*Boa constrictor imperator*) occurs from northern Sonora and central Tamaulipas, Mexico, through Central America to northwestern and western Colombia, western Ecuador and northwestern Peru (Stimson, 1969). *Boa c. imperator* has a darker overall coloration and is usually smaller than the common Colombian boa. Although *Boa c. imperator* is frequently available through the pet trade, it is considered to have a bad disposition.

Captive husbandry and propagation for the true red-tail *Boa constrictor* subspecies can be more complicated than that of *Boa c. constrictor,* or *Boa c. imperator.* Chiras (1979) observed copulation among captive red-tail boas from early December through early May, with parturition occurring late July through late August.

The Bolivian red-tail boa constrictor (*Boa constrictor amarali*) occurs in southern and southwestern Brazil, as well as southeastern Bolivia (Peters and Orejas-Miranda, 1970). The common name of Bolivian red-tail stems from the fact that most captive specimens in the United States were exported from Bolivia. *Boa c. amarali* is relatively small, rarely exceeding 2 m (6.5 ft) in total length.

Goergen (pers. comm.) has observed copulation among captive *Boa c. amarali* from late December through mid-March, and parturition in early September. A litter of 14 young, 11 stillborn, and two infertile ova was recorded. The live neonates were observed being expelled from the female first. The stillborn and infertile ova followed, with the entire process taking 5–6 hours. It was noted that the neonates were not contained within their membrane sacs when expelled by the female, which may have been due to the lengthy process or a late parturition date.

The Peruvian red-tail boa (*Boa constrictor ortoni*) is found in northwestern Peru. Mehrtens (1987) mentions a 13' 7" (4.5 m) captive *Boa c. ortoni.*

In captivity the true red-tail boas are susceptible to regurgitation problems. Maintaining red-tails at slightly higher temperatures than those described for common Colombian boas will frequently resolve this problem. In addition relative humidity levels should be maintained at a minimum of 85% to avoid dehydration. It is also wise to avoid feeding comparatively large food animals to red-tails. I believe that many of the husbandry problems, as well as the lack of breeding success associated with true red-tail boas in captivity, can be attributed to the fact that most herpetoculturists are working with wild-caught imports. Stress and internal parasite loads have led to the death of many imported red-tails.

The Hogg Island boa from Honduras or small islands offshore is a small *Boa constrictor*, with adults measuring about 2 m (6 ft) in length. They have ability to change color from light to dark. Although the Hogg Island boa does not have subspecific designation, it is well known by herpetoculturists. Goergen (pers. comm.) has observed copulation during January, with parturition occurring from late May through mid-July. The largest recorded litter consisted of 20 young, one stillborn, and one infertile ova.

The Argentine boa (*Boa constrictor occidentalis*) occurs in Argentina and Paraguay. It is a very attractive boa with a silver background coloration. *Boa c. occidentalis* is being regularly reproduced in captivity. Goergen (pers. comm.) has observed copulation late January through early April, with the majority of observed copulations occurring late February through mid-March. Parturition has been observed late July through late August. The largest recorded litter consisted of 24 young.

The Saboga Island boa (*Boa constrictor sabogae*) is found on Saboga Island in the Gulf of Panama, and is quite scarce in captive collections.

The black-bellied boa (*Boa constrictor melanogaster*) was described by Langhammer (1983) as occurring in Ecuador. There are doubts as to the validity of this subspecies.

The sigma boa (*Boa constrictor sigma*) was described by Smith (1943) as occurring on Tres Marias Island, Mexico. This subspecies has since been considered identical to *Boa c. imperator*, and is no longer a valid subspecies.

The black *Boa constrictor* or long-tail *Boa constrictor* (*Boa constrictor longicauda*) was described by Price and Russo (1991) as occurring from the vicinity of Tumbes, Peru. *Boa c. longicauda* differs from all other *Boa constrictor* subspecies by possessing a longer tail (in the male) and hemipenis, and a unique color pattern. *Boa c. longicauda* is geographically isolated by mountains.

Lazell (1964) discussed the *Boa constrictor* from two islands in the Lesser Antilles—St. Lucia, and Dominica. The St. Lucia Island boa (*Boa constrictor orophias*) differs in squamation (scale count and arrangement) from *Boa c. constrictor*. *Boa constrictor orophias* is also darker with more of an irregular pattern, and a more prominent snout. As in *Boa c. constrictor*, juveniles tend to be more arboreal than adults. Young specimens of *Boa c. orophias* have been found in trees as high as 12 m (39.5 ft).

The Dominican Island or clouded boa (*Boa constrictor nebulosus*) is a very dark grey-brown color (clouded) dorsally. Its pattern is comprised of light irregular markings and appear more as mottling than actual transverse saddles. *Boa c. nebulosus* has a more prominent snout than *Boa c. constrictor*, and a concave canthus (side of the snout, between the tip of the snout and the eye). Both *Boa c. orophias* and *Boa c. nebulosus* are being worked with in captivity, and should be more common in captive collections in the near future.

Rainbow Boas (*Epicrates cenchria* subspecies)

The rainbow boa (*Epicrates cenchria*) complex consists of nine subspecies (Ross and Marzec, 1990). Rainbow boas are highly iridescent, the myriad of colors being most vivid just after ecdysis. Rainbow boas are powerful constrictors with sizable teeth. In the wild, mammals and birds are the preferred prey. Like some other boids, rainbow boas possess heat-sensing labial pits. Males are equipped with well-developed anal spurs which are utilized during courtship.

This account concentrates on the three subspecies which are the most commonly maintained in captivity. The Brazilian rainbow boa (*Epicrates cenchria cenchria*), the Colombian rainbow boa (*Epicrates cenchria maurus*), and the Argentine rainbow boa (*Epicrates cenchria alvarezi*).

The Brazilian rainbow boa (*E. c. cenchria*) occurs in southern Venezuela, Guyana, and Surinam, and south through the Amazon Basin (Mehrtens, 1987). The preferred habitats are tropical forests, woodlands, and adjacent savannahs. *E. c. cenchria* is one of the largest subspecies and can attain a length of over 2 m (6.5 ft). It is also usually considered the most attractive of the rainbow boas. Individuals are frequently a brilliant orange or red background color, with connecting dark ocelli comprising the dorsal pattern. Light-colored lateral crescents appear on most specimens.

Brazilian rainbow boas are hardy captives when their requirements are properly met. High humidity is crucial. A minimum relative humidity of 85% should be provided throughout the day, with a maximum drop of only 10% at night. A high humidity habitat for all rainbow boas can be achieved by using a damp astroturf substrate. The astroturf should be of the high-quality cloth, woven-backed variety. When a heat tape or galvanized metal heat pad is placed beneath a portion of the rainbow boa enclosure the damp turf substrate raises the relative humidity through evaporation. Water should be added to the astroturf as needed to maintain high humidity. Water will be absorbed by the astroturf and should not be allowed to pool on the surface. A water bowl large enough for complete soaking, half-filled with clean water, should be provided at all times.

Neodesha plastics enclosures are ideal for housing rainbow boas. Plastic shoebox, sweaterbox, and the 24 inch (61 cm) Neodesha models will comfortably house a neonate through small juvenile rainbow boa. The 36 inch (91 cm) model will accommodate most adults. The 48 inch (122 cm) model can properly house rainbow boas of 1.5 m (5 ft) total length and larger. All enclosure models support high humidity conditions extremely well due to their reduced ventilation design. If high relative humidity is not provided, Brazilian rainbow boas may suffer from dehydration, respiratory problems, and skin ailments, with regurgitation and even death as a result. As with any warm, high humidity reptile enclosure, frequent servicing is necessary to maintain sanitary conditions. Although rainbow boas are semiarboreal, it is not necessary to supply climbing facilities for captives.

The recommended temperature range for *E. c. cenchria* falls between 21–32°C (70°–90°F). When Brazilian rainbow boas are exposed to temperatures above 32°C (90°F), regurgitation may occur. Temperatures below 21°C (70°F) will lead to respiratory ailments. An ambient temperature of 26°C (78°–80°F) is ideal. The enclosure should be equipped with a heat tape or heat pad positioned beneath one-third to one- half of the floor. This should provide a warm substrate area of 32–35°C (90°–95°F). This allows rainbow boas to thermoregulate by moving on or off the heated portion of the enclosure. A nighttime temperature drop of 2°C (5°F) is desirable. This may be accomplished by connecting the heat tape or heat pad to an automatic timer. The timer should be set in conjunction with the photoperiod to allow the heating device to operate during the daylight hours. If the room temperature is not within the preferred temperature range, the heat tape or pad can be operated at a lesser temperature, as opposed to being completely turned off.

Captive reproduction of *Epicrates cenchria cenchria* is fairly commonplace. Goergen (pers. comm.) has observed copulation from mid-December through late May, with the majority of observed copulations occurring from early January through late March. Goergen has observed parturition from early July through early October.

Of 20 recorded *E. c. cenchria* births, 16 occurred during the months of October and November. A litter of 35 viable young was recorded September 1994. Goergen (pers. comm.) cycled *E. c. cenchria* at temperatures as low as 20°C (68°F); Hine (1989) cycled specimens to 15°C (59°F). Normally it is not recommended to subject specimens to cycling temperatures below 21°C (70°F), as respiratory ailments may occur.

Brazilian rainbow boas are rarely problem feeders. Neonate *E. c. cenchria* can be offered fuzzy (one week old) mice immediately after their first shed. A 7–10 day feeding schedule for neonates and juveniles is adequate. Adult rainbow boas should be fed an appropriately-sized rodent on a 10 day to 2 week schedule. Freshly-killed or stunned rodents will be accepted by the majority of rainbow boas. It may be necessary to simulate rodent movement with the aid of forceps or tongs. Rainbow boas are primarily nocturnal. If a problem feeder is encountered, it is beneficial to attempt feeding under red light.

The Colombian rainbow boa (*Epicrates cenchria maurus*) inhabits portions of Costa Rica, Colombia, Venezuela, northern Guyana, Trinidad and Tobago, and Margarita (Perez-Santos and Moreno, 1988). *Epicrates cenchria maurus* ranges in dorsal coloration from light brown to dark brownish purple. Most adults are uniform in color, although specimens with a faint pattern of dark round blotches may be encountered. The pattern is much more pronounced in juvenile Colombian rainbow boas, resembling that of *E. c. cenchria*. Adult *E. c. maurus* are typically 1.5 m (4–5 ft) in total length. It is recommended that *E. c. maurus* be maintained at a slightly higher temperature than *E. c. cenchria*. A temperature range of 28–29°C (83°–85°F) is ideal. Although high humidity is important for *E. c. maurus*, it is not as crucial as for *E. c. cenchria*. Management of Colombian rainbow boas is similar to that outlined for the Brazilian rainbow boas.

In captivity, *E. c. maurus* typically breed earlier in the year than *E. c. cenchria*. I have observed copulation between a single pair of *E. c. maurus* during October, which resulted in a parturition date of April 15. Goergen (pers. comm.) observed copulation during November and December, with parturition occurring from late May through early July. A litter of 23 viable young was recorded May 1987.

The Argentine rainbow boa (*Epicrates cenchria alvarezi*) inhabits the forest areas of Argentina. The ground color varies from tan to brownish. The dorsal pattern is comprised of connecting dark saddles forming irregularly shaped light-colored circular markings. *Epicrates cenchria alvarezi* is far less common in captive collections than the previous two subspecies. In captivity, it is also more secretive. While a hide box will be utilized periodically by the Brazilian and Colombian rainbow boas, it is a necessity for the Argentine rainbow boa. Neonate *E. c. alvarezi* can be problem feeders. In my experience, some neonates will accept pink or small fuzzy (newborn to one week old) mice as their first meal, while others show no interest. Small lizards should be offered to specimens refusing mice. Husbandry for adult Argentine rainbow boas should be approached similarly to that for the Brazilian rainbow boa.

Epicrates cenchria alvarezi have been reproduced in relatively small numbers in captivity. Few data have been recorded as to propagation. I observed copulation among *E. c. alvarezi* during early December. Goergen (pers. comm.) has observed copulation during December, which resulted in a litter of nine viable young on August 15.

Female rainbow boas may consume newly born infertile ova, and stillborn young (Ross and Marzec, 1990). I have observed this behavior in *E. c. alvarezi* and Goergen (pers. comm.) has observed this in *E. c. cenchria*.

Postpartum interest of a female *E. c. cenchria* toward its newborn young was exhibited by a specimen at the National Zoological Park in Washington, D.C. This consisted of her prodding the young, which were encased in their fetal membranes. This continued until all the young were free of their sacs (Walsh and Davis, 1983).

Emerald Tree Boa (*Corallus caninus*)

The emerald tree boa (*Corallus caninus*) is one of the world's most attractive, unusual, and interesting snake species. A small to medium size boa, adult specimens typically measure 1.5 m (4–5 ft) in total length. Emerald tree boas inhabit the tropical rainforest regions of Colombia, Venezuela, Brazil, Ecuador, Bolivia, Surinam, Peru, the Amazon basin, and Guyana Shield regions.

Corallus caninus from the Amazon basin and Guyana Shield tend to differ from each other in scalation and color, with Amazon specimens generally having smaller prefrontal, frontal, and internasal scales than Guyanan specimens (Walsh, pers. comm.).

Emeralds are a rich green color dorsally with a white, yellow, or gold venter. The majority of emerald tree boas sport white dorsal markings, although I have maintained an adult female which was solid green dorsally. The dorsal markings can range from flecks to a complete white vertebral stripe which is seen on Amazon basin specimens. Guyanan Shield specimens are often marked with gray middorsal bars. Ditmars (1931) suggested that the white dorsal markings serve as camouflage in simulating patches of light coming through the foliage.

When considering the acquisition of emerald tree boas, only captive-produced specimens should be chosen. *Corallus caninus* is a delicate and easily stressed species. Wild-caught imported specimens do not readily adapt to captivity, and the majority do not survive the first few months.

Housing for the emerald tree boa is designed around its arboreal lifestyle. When choosing an enclosure, height is an important consideration. Wooden epoxy-painted enclosures approximately 1 m wide, 40 cm deep, and 1 m high (3 ft × 16 in × 3 ft) can comfortably house an adult emerald. Front-opening glass or acrylic panels aid in the servicing of a tall enclosure. Tall glass terraria fitted with screen covers can be adapted for emerald tree boa housing.

The enclosure should be equipped with several branches, with a diameter at least as large as the emerald at midbody, to comfortably support the snake. Smooth materials such as polyvinyl chloride (PVC) pipe and bamboo should be avoided. Branches with surface irregularities allow a more secure grip. Several branches at different heights should be incorporated into the enclosure. All branches should be positioned high enough above the enclosure floor to allow the emerald to hang down in a "J" configuration while feeding without touching the floor. The branches may rest on blocks of wood attached to opposite sides of the enclosure, or may be anchored using screw eyes and hooks. Wagner (1985) utilized wooden dowel rods suspended in "U" shaped clips which were attached with silicone rubber to opposite ends of the terraria. Only a 100% silicone sealant should be used for reptile enclosures, as some silicone sealants contain fungicides which may be toxic. Dowel rods or branches should be securely positioned and unable to rotate. These enclosures are most easily serviced by removing the entire branch with the snake resting upon it. Unwinding the emerald from the branch or trying to manipulate it with snake sticks will cause stress to the snake.

An overhead heat source such as a 40–60 watt incandescent bulb within a reflector or ceramic element should be positioned at one end of the enclosure. This will allow the emerald tree boa to thermoregulate, by moving to a higher branch near the heat source, or further from the heat source on lower branches. The uppermost branch should be 35°C (95°F) at least at one end (if the branch angles toward the heat source). The cooler portion of the enclosure should be 27°C (80°F).

High humidity levels must be maintained within the emerald's enclosure. A minimum of 85% will prevent respiratory and shedding problems. A heat tape or galvanized metal heat pad positioned beneath a damp astroturf substrate will produce the necessary humidity. Misting of warm water via a commercial misting system or hand sprayer should be a daily routine. Many emeralds will not drink from a water bowl, but will drink water droplets from enclosure walls, branches, and body coils. Misting also helps maintain necessary humidity levels. It is a good idea to provide a water bowl filled with clean water on the floor of the enclosure at all times, as I have observed some emeralds drinking from a bowl.

I believe that except for public displays, no plants (live or artificial) are necessary for captive emerald tree boa enclosures. Huff (pers. comm.) described a captive emerald tree boa death which resulted from ingestion of an artificial plant leaf. If additional security is desired, hide areas can be produced by covering portions of the enclosure front or sides with contact paper, as well as a temporary cover of cloth or paper.

Corallus caninus is a nocturnal species and feeding attempts should be made at night. Adult emerald tree boas can be offered large mice or small rats. It is preferable to feed freshly-killed rodents offered from forceps. This can be attempted at night under red lights. If the emerald seems uninterested, the head of the rodent can be heated with a light bulb and reintroduced. Another method which can prove effective is to "tickle" or manipulate the tail of the emerald while moving the rodent in front of the snake's head. The annoyance may induce the emerald to strike and coil the rodent. If these attempts fail, a live rodent can be placed in the emerald's enclosure just prior to the room lights being switched off. Frequent checks can be made under red light to see if feeding has occurred. If mice and juvenile rats are not accepted, chicks or quail can also be offered. If all else fails small hamsters can be offered.

Captive *Corallus caninus* are notorious for their tendency to regurgitate. Funk (1987) cites cryptosporidiosis as the primary cause of emerald tree boa regurgitation. Ross (1989) believes that regurgitation syndrome in emeralds is a result of many causes, including infectious agents and suboptimal husbandry practices. At present this condition is not curable, ultimately fatal, and highly contagious among emerald tree boas. Large meals and overfeeding can cause regurgitation. Rodents that are larger than the diameter of the emerald at mid-body should not be offered. Overfeeding should also be avoided. Digestion and elimination in emerald tree boas typically takes 2–3 weeks. Waiting until the previous meal is passed before feeding again is a good rule of thumb. The use of rodents as food can also contribute to regurgitation problems. Ditmars (1931) states that in the wild, tree boas feed largely on birds. Walsh (unpublished manuscript) mentions that chicks are occasionally fed to emerald tree boas at the National Zoo, and appear to serve as a natural laxative. In the wild *Corallus caninus* are shown feeding on birds, (Mitchell, 1986) commonly small parrot species. Beebe (1946) includes "Parrot Snake" as a common name, implying that emerald tree boas feed on parrots. Schmidt and Inger (1957) mention that the emerald tree boa feeds largely on birds, and needs its long and strong front teeth to make certain of their capture. This contrasts with the primarily rodent diets that maintain most captives. Stress and low humidity and temperature levels can also contribute to regurgitation problems.

Captive emeralds occasionally suffer from intestinal blockages. This disorder can be especially hazardous for neonates, as a prolapse of the cloaca may occur. If a noticeable bulge or swelling is evident just above the vent, and the tail is hanging below the branch, a blockage may be present. A container of warm water should be positioned beneath the branch so that the tail is submerged past the vent. The soaking should allow the blockage to pass. I believe that intestinal blockages are a product of captivity. Reduced movement due to confined housing and an unnatural diet may be the greatest contributors.

Captive *Corallus caninus* reproduction is not commonplace, but several zoological institutions as well as herpetoculturists have achieved success. In captivity *Corallus caninus* can be manipulated to breed at any time of the year. Weidner (1986) observed copulation between captive pairs of emeralds during early March, and mid-April through late May. Copulation was observed by Moyle and Ross (1991) in September and October, and by Goergen (pers. comm.) in mid-January through late

February. Walsh (unpublished manuscript) witnessed a birth from a wild-caught gravid female late October. The majority of North American emerald breeders have achieved breeding success by cycling their captives from December through February.

Emerald tree boa copulation will take place with both snakes positioned on a branch. Gravid females will show signs of mid-body swelling, and a shrunken or collapsed appearance of the rear sides of the head. Large branches, preferably with a flat upper surface, should be provided to support gravid females. A hot spot of at least 35–37°C (95°–100°F) should be available for gravid emeralds.

Weidner (1986) recorded *Corallus caninus* gestation periods of 210 and 215 days; Tepedelen (1989) recorded one of 259 days. Goergen (pers. comm.) reports captive parturition dates from mid-October through late December, with litter size ranging from five to eleven young. Of eight recorded litters, half consisted of six or seven young.

Female emerald tree boas should have good body weight prior to captive propagation attempts. It is not uncommon for gravid emeralds to refuse food throughout the entire gestation period.

Neonate *Corallus caninus* are highly variable in coloration. Goergen (pers. comm.) has observed all green litters of *Corallus caninus*, as well as all orange/red litters, and others which included a mixture of each. Ross and Marzec (1990) make reference to young of yellow coloration.

Neonate emerald tree boas can be problem feeders. They can be housed individually in plastic or glass 1 gal wide mouth jars. A damp paper towel should cover the entire bottom of the jar. A small branch or wooden dowel rod secured only 5–8 cm (2–3 in) above the jar floor must be included. The jar should rest upon a heat tape or galvanized heat pad. The jar lid should be drilled (from the inside out) with 24 ⅛ inch diameter holes. After the neonate has completed its first ecdysis, during the evening a live 1–2 week old (fuzzy) mouse (fuzzies are usually preferred over newborn mice by neonate emeralds) can be placed in the bottom of the jar just prior to the room lights being switched off. Neonates will rest in typical emerald tree boa fashion with symmetrical coils draped over the branch or dowel with the head suspended downward slightly below the body. With no corners to the gallon jar, the fuzzy mouse will exhibit more movement and be seized when passing just under the emerald's nose and heat-sensing facial pits. After several feedings have taken place, the neonate can be moved to a larger enclosure, and the forceps feeding method described earlier can be attempted with freshly killed fuzzy mice.

I hope in the near future more *Corallus caninus* natural history information will be published. This will aid in the captive husbandry and propagation of this fascinating species.

Amazon and Cook's Tree Boa (*Corallus enydris enydris, Corallus enydris cooki*)

Corallus enydris are arboreal, nocturnal boas which occur from southern Costa Rica to southern Brazil and on several oceanic islands (including St. Vincent and the Grenada bank). The Amazon tree boa (*Corallus enydris enydris*) is the southern form, occurring in Amazonian and Guyanan sections of the mainland. The Cook's tree boa (*Corallus enydris cooki*) is the northern form, occurring in Central America, extreme northern South America, and some West Indian islands. *C. e. cooki* inhabits a wider range of habitats and climate regimes than does *C. e. enydris* (Henderson and Winstel, 1995).

Corallus enydris are extremely variable in color and pattern. The geographic area in which the boa occurs is responsible for the main elements of dorsal pattern (Henderson, 1991). On Grenada color varies at different altitudes (Henderson, 1990). Ross and Marzec (1990) state that a female of any of the color morphs can produce young of every color and pattern variation.

Captive husbandry for *Corallus enydris* is similar to that of *Corallus caninus*. *Corallus enydris* is a much hardier captive and presents few of the problems encountered with *Corallus caninus*. The main drawback to captive *Corallus enydris* is their disposition, as most captive specimens have a tendency to strike at any moving object. It may be necessary to partially or completely cover transparent portions of enclosures housing *Corallus enydris*, as the boas may injure themselves by hitting glass, screens, etc. while striking at movement near the enclosure.

Winstel (1989) observed captive *Corallus enydris enydris* intertwined (apparently copulating) during the months of February, March, and April. Parturition has been recorded in November and December. Litter size is typically from seven to fifteen.

Schwartz and Henderson (1991) examined various female *Corallus enydris cooki* on Grenada, one of which contained 17 near full-term young on June 18. Two others contained 29 undeveloped ova on May 13, and 40 ova on May 16.

Adult captive *Corallus enydris* typically feed on mice, rats, and chicks. Captive neonates often accept fuzzy mice as their first meal. Reluctant neonates should be offered small *Anolis* lizards.

Annulated Boa (*Corallus annulatus*)

The annulated boa (*Corallus annulatus*) is primarily arboreal and attains a total length of 2 m (6 ft). *Corallus annulatus* occurs from central and eastern Nicaragua through Colombia to Ecuador on both sides of the Andes (Peters and Orejas-Miranda, 1970).

Adult annulated boa coloration ranges from light tan to brownish red, patterned with blackish rings or netlike reticulations.

Corallus annulatus is not as strictly arboreal as *C. caninus* and captives will utilize hide boxes on the enclosure floor. Blody and Mehaffey (1989) mention *Corallus annulatus* temperament as being relatively mild, and more like that of *Sanzinia* than *Corallus caninus* or *C. enydris*.

Captive husbandry for *Corallus annulatus* can be approached similarly to that of *Corallus caninus*. The main difference is in feeding reluctant eaters. When offering the annulated boa freshly-killed rodents (from tongs or forceps) a slow, gentle approach should be used. This contrasts with the emerald tree boa which may feed while being antagonized.

Wild-caught *Corallus annulatus* have given birth to seven young in August and fifteen young in October. An additional wild-caught female gave birth on November 30 (Ross and Marzec, 1990).

Blody and Mehaffey (1989) observed copulation among captive *C. annulatus* from mid-December through late March, with parturition occurring late July through mid-October. Litters ranging in size from 8 to 15 have been recorded.

Neonate coloration ranges from brick red to burnt orange. Neonate *C. annulatus* typically accept unweaned mice or hatchling quail for their first meal. Frozen, thawed tree frogs (*Hyla* spp.) and lizards (*Basiliscus plumifrons*) may also be accepted, as well as scented mice (Blody and Mehaffey, 1989).

Insular *Epicrates*

The "insular *Epicrates*" consist of nine species of boas which are isolated on small oceanic islands. Endemic species include the Ford's boa (*E. fordi*) and vine boa (*E. gracilis*), both of which inhabit Hispaniola, Cuban boa (*E. angulifer*), Jamaican boa (*E. subflavus*), Puerto Rican boa (*E. inornatus*), and the Abaco Island boa (*E. exsul.*). *Epicrates chrysogaster, E. monensis,* and *E. striatus* have more scattered distributions on the southern Bahamas, the Puerto Bank, and Hispaniola and the Great Bahama Bank, respectively (Tolson, 1994). Although these boas vary greatly in size, appearance, preferred habitat and diet, there are many similarities in successful captive husbandry and propagation practices.

Several species of insular *Epicrates* are in danger of extinction. Habitat destruction, the introduction of the black rat (*Rattus rattus*), house cat (*Felis catus*), and Indian mongoose (*Herpestes griseus*), and overcollecting are the primary threats to species such as *Epicrates subflavus, E. monensis, E. inornatus,* and *E. striatus fosteri.*

Hide boxes should be incorporated into enclosures which house insular *Epicrates*. Many species are semi-arboreal and will benefit from sturdy branches on which they can climb. Neodesha Plastics enclosures of the appropriate size make ideal housing for the majority of captive *Epicrates*. An astroturf substrate is recommended where high relative humidity is desired.

Most adult specimens will voluntarily feed upon an appropriately sized rodent or chick. Tolson (1994) reports that adult *Epicrates fordi, E. gracilis,* and *E. monensis* prefer *Anolis* lizards to mice or rats. Neonate and juvenile specimens are typically lizard eaters and often must be provided with small lizards for at least the first few feedings. If pink mice are still rejected after the boa has consumed several lizards, scenting techniques can be initiated. Tolson (1994) recommends tube feeding a high calorie (about 28 calories per gram) dietary supplement, such as Nutri-cal (Evso Pharmaceuticals, Buena, NJ 08310) to neonate insular *Epicrates* specimens which refuse to feed voluntarily. Tube feeding is required before neonate boas lose more than 33% of their birth weight. As insular *Epicrates* are primarily nocturnal, food should be offered to reluctant feeders under red light or dark conditions.

Most species of insular *Epicrates* shed their skin immediately after birth. The second shed typically occurs at approximately 2 weeks of age. Feeding attempts should be made shortly after this second ecdysis.

Tolson (1994) reports that most species of insular *Epicrates* begin courtship in February. *E. fordi* begins courtship in late December or early January, and *E. angulifer* normally courts in May or June.

Male combat can play an important role in captive insular *Epicrates* reproduction. Males can be introduced into a breeding enclosure during or after temperature cycling in order to initiate male combat. During combat male insular *Epicrates* typically release a pungent musk from their cloacal glands and may coil around each other. After combative behavior is observed among males one or more females can be introduced into the enclosure. Care should be taken to prevent injury by larger males to smaller ones during the breeding season. Females may also become aggressive toward males. Tolson (1994) reports an adult female *E. inornatus* killing and consuming a male at the Toledo Zoological Gardens, and a similar incident occurring with a pair of *E. subflavus* at the Columbus Zoological Gardens. I observed an adult female *E. subflavus* which had recently grasped a male's head with her mouth and completely coiled around his body, apparently constricting him. This behavior occurred with a single pair (the only two *E. subflavus* in the collection) which had been copulating sporadically the prior 2 weeks with no apparent problem prior to this episode.

Hide areas such as damp, layered sphagnum moss should be incorporated into the gravid female's enclosure as she nears parturition. This can provide refuge for newly born neonates. In captivity, females may devour living young after birth (Tolson, 1992).

Litter size in *Epicrates* corresponds to the size of the female. The larger the female of any given species, the larger the litter size (Tolson, 1994).

The Cuban boa (*Epicrates angulifer*) is a large semi-arboreal species which is widely distributed throughout Cuba. Tolson and Henderson (1993) report a female measuring in excess of 5 m (15 ft, 11 in) was killed on a road on the U.S. Naval Base, Guantanamo Bay, Cuba, in 1989.

Tolson (1980b) observed copulation among captive *E. angulifer* during June, with parturition occurring during February of the following year. Five or six young was a typical litter size. Huff (1976) observed copulation among captive *E. angulifer* March 10 through April 12. Parturition occurred September 16, with one live young, one stillborn, and four infertile ova being produced. Hamper (pers. comm.) observed captive copulation late March, with parturition occurring mid-October through early November. Litters of nine and seven viable young were recorded, as well as a litter consisting of one live young and eleven infertile ova.

Neonate *E. angulifer* usually accept small rodents as their first meals.

The Puerto Rican boa (*Epicrates inornatus*) is a semi-arboreal inhabitant of rain forest, karst forest, caves, and plantations of Puerto Rico. *E. inornatus* was one of the first species protected by the U.S. Endangered Species Act of 1973. It is also listed as Appendix I in CITES (Convention on International Trade in Endangered Species).

Tolson and Henderson (1993) report most mating of wild *E. inornatus* occurs at the beginning of the wet season (late April through May).

Huff (1978) reports maintaining captive *E. inornatus* at 26–30°C (79–86°F) for the majority of the year, but adults were cycled at 20°C (75°F) for 5–10 days prior to a breeding attempt. *E. inornatus* are biennial breeders in captivity. Females with a minimum total length of 160 cm (62 inches) and an approximate weight of 1 kg (2.2 lb) are sexually mature and capable of producing young. Smaller males are capable of reproducing (Huff, 1978).

Hamper (pers. comm.) observed copulation among captive

E. inornatus late March, with parturition occurring late August. Litters numbering 11 and 16 were recorded. Huff (1978) reports copulation among captives from March through April, but recorded copulation as late as June. A gestation period of 153–176 days was recorded, with a litter of 21 being produced. A captive female maintained at the Toledo Zoological Gardens gave birth to 10 young on August 5 (Tolson and Henderson, 1993).

Tolson and Henderson (1993) report wild neonate *E. inornatus* feed almost exclusively on *Anolis* and arboreal *Eleutherodactylus* frogs. At night wild *E. inornatus* hang from vines and crevices at the mouths of caves and seize and devour bats emerging from the caves (Nelson, 1994). Nelson (1994) reports that *E. inornatus* have been observed consuming the remains of bats killed by feral cats.

The Jamaican boa (*Epicrates subflavus*) is a semi-arboreal inhabitant of the forests of Jamaica. *E. subflavus* occurs in the parishes of St. Thomas and Trelawny, and has also been observed on Goat Island in the Heathshire Hills (Barbour, 1910). The Jamaican boa is an endangered species and is listed in Appendix I of CITES.

Epicrates subflavus is a medium size boa. Adult females are larger than males, averaging approximately 2 m (6 ft) in total length. Lynn and Grant (1940) report a specimen which measured in excess of 3 m (9.5 ft).

Bloxam (1977) observed copulation among captive *E. subflavus* from late February through late June, with the majority of recorded copulation occurring from mid- to late May. Parturition occurred on September 21 and November 8, with litters of 24 and 34 young, respectively. Hamper (pers. comm.) observed copulation among captives from February through March, with parturition occurring October through early November. Litters of 23 viable young and two infertile ova, 15 viable young, four stillborn and one infertile ova, and 13 viable young, two stillborn and eight infertile ova were recorded.

Neonate *E. subflavus* typically accept pink mice as their first meals. Bloxam (1977) reports neonates that initially refused pink mice accepted the pinks when they were smeared with a day-old chick.

Epicrates chrysogaster schwartzi occurs in the Bahama Islands,

Acklins Island, and Crooked Island (Tolson and Henderson, 1993). Buden (1975) reports a wild-caught *E. chrysogaster schwartzi* collected from North Caicos on June 5 that gave birth to 28 young on September 14–15. An adult pair held at the University of Michigan copulated on July 4, with parturition occurring February 27 of the following year. A litter of nine young was recorded after a 238 day gestation period (Tolson, 1980b).

Epicrates exsul inhabits pinewoods on the Bahama Islands, Grand Bahama Island, Great Abaco Island (including Elbow Cay and Green Turtle Cay), and Little Abaco Island (Tolson and Henderson, 1993).

Tolson and Henderson (1993) report a 234 gram (4 ounce) female *E. exsul* maintained at the Toledo Zoological Gardens giving birth to nine young on August 20.

The Ford's boa (*Epicrates fordi fordi*) occurs in Hispaniola.

Murphy and Guese (1977) report a subadult pair of *E. f. fordi* found near Port-au-Prince, Haiti, under small rocks at the base of rocky ledges. At the Dallas Zoo the boas readily accepted small mice weekly, while being maintained at an ambient temperature ranging from 27–38°C (81–100°F) and a relative humidity of 50%.

Copulation was observed January 30, with parturition occurring July 6. A litter of five young was produced. At 2 weeks of age four neonates began feeding on *Anolis* and *Uta* lizards, with the fifth accepting newborn mice. All but one neonate were switched to newborn mice.

The Virgin Islands boa (*Epicrates monensis granti*) occurs in the U.S. and British Virgin Islands. The Virgin Islands boa is an endangered species and is listed in Appendix I of CITES.

Tolson (1989) reports increasing relative humidity levels after temperature cycling for captive *E. monensis granti* to add stimuli for breeding. Tolson and Henderson (1993) report that no male combat has been observed for this species unlike other species of insular *Epicrates.*

Tolson (1989) observed courtship behavior among captive *E. monensis granti* from February through May. Copulation was observed March 10. Parturition occurred from mid-July through mid-September, with a recorded gestation period of 132 days. Tolson (1988) reports that in the wild, gravid *E. monensis* maintain body temperatures of 30–33°C (86–91°F) during basking.

Tolson (1980b) observed copulation among captive *Epicrates striatus* during February, with parturition occurring September 22. A litter of 12 viable young and four infertile ova was produced. An additional female gave birth to 21 young and three infertile ova on October 10.

Bartlett (1990) reports a nearly 2.5 m (8 ft) long captive Bimini boa (*Epicrates striatus fosteri*) giving birth to 29 viable young and several infertile ova.

Anacondas (*Eunectes murinus, Eunectes notaeus*)

This account concentrates on the two species within the genus *Eunectes* which are the most commonly maintained in captivity. The green anaconda (*Eunectes murinus*) and the yellow anaconda (*Eunectes notaeus*).

Eunectes murinus is a semi-aquatic inhabitant of lowland rainforests near bodies of water including rivers, streams, lakes, ponds, ditches, temporary pools, and flooded forests. In addition *E. murinus* occurs in areas such as dry forest and the llanos, due to the abundance of surface water in these areas for 6–8 months of the year during the wet season (Strimple, 1993).

The green anaconda is the heaviest and possibly the longest snake in the world. Ten m (30 ft) in length and a weight in excess of 270 kg (600 lb) may be achieved by this giant boid.

Oftentimes in the wild *E. murinus* will lay submerged in wait of prey which may drink at the water's edge. In addition to being constricted, the prey may also succumb to drowning. In the wild prey consists of a variety of vertebrates including amphibians, fish, reptiles, birds, and mammals.

Although there is controversy as to their validity, it is widely accepted that two subspecies of *Eunectes murinus* exist. *Eunectes murinus murinus* is the southern form occurring throughout the Amazonian drainage in Peru, Brazil, and northern Bolivia. *Eunectes murinus gigas* is the northern form occurring in Ecuador, Colombia, Venezuela, the Guianas, and Trinidad.

The green anaconda has a somewhat bad reputation among herpetoculturists. Wild-caught adult specimens typically possess a bad disposition; however, captive born specimens do not usually display this behavior.

Adult *E. murinus* require large enclosures which can be custom built or an entire room can be prepared to function as an enclosure. Newspaper or bark chips are recommended as a substrate for large anaconda enclosures.

A large tub half filled with clean water should be present within the enclosure at all times. The tub should be large enough for the anaconda to completely submerge without displacing too much water. The water tub may also be utilized by anacondas for breeding. Plastic or fiberglass tubs are recommended. Rubbermaid agricultural troughs are ideal, as they are nontoxic and equipped with a threaded drain and plug. The Rubbermaid troughs are available in sizes as large as 1137 L (300 gal). Galvanized tubs should be avoided unless thoroughly sealed with an epoxy paint, as galvanized steel can add toxins to drinking water. I have also experienced holes forming in some galvanized tubs. It is advantageous to connect the water tub to a floor drain, as anacondas will often defecate in the water. It is much less labor intensive to open a valve and rinse the tub than it is to siphon out the water. It is important to keep the anaconda's water source very clean, as captives will spend a great deal of time submerged. If the water source is not maintained properly blister disease may develop. Frye (1981) describes blister disease as the clinical manifestation of necrotic dermatitis resulting from infection with a plethora of bacteria and fungi. Neonate and juvenile anacondas are especially susceptible.

In captivity *Eunectes murinus* will feed on mice, rats, guinea pigs, rabbits and pigs. Chickens and waterfowl can be fed as a supplement and to entice reluctant feeders. As a last resort amphibians or fish can be offered or used for scenting. I maintained a subadult *E. murinus* for several years which fed voraciously on guinea pigs, but refused all other mammals.

As a safety precaution the keeper should have at least one assistant present when feeding adult *E. murinus* or servicing their enclosures.

Strimple (1986) observed copulation among captive *Eunectes murinus* from late April through late June. Parturition was recorded December 24, December 26, and January 18 (Strimple, 1994). Litters of 16 viable young and two infertile ova, 21 viable young and 14 infertile ova, and 30 viable young, four stillborn and three infertile ova were recorded. Deschanel (1978) observed copulation occurring in the water among captive *E. murinus* during July, with parturition occurring March 8. Parturition also took place in the water, with 14 viable young and one stillborn being produced. The neonate's first ecdysis occurred within 5–8 days.

Strimple (1994) reports the majority of his captive born *Eunectes murinus* feed voluntarily after their first ecdysis on live rat pinks and mouse fuzzies.

The yellow anaconda (*Eunectes notaeus*) is a semi-aquatic boa that rarely exceeds 4 m (12 ft) in total length. *E. notaeus* occurs in Bolivia, Paraguay, Uruguay, western Brazil and northeastern Argentina (Peters and Orejas-Miranda, 1970).

Holstrom (1981) observed the majority of copulation among captive *E. notaeus* from November through January. Courtship occurred on land as well as within the water. Parturition occurred late April through mid-October, with litters of 6, 10 and 12 young being produced. The females showed post-parturient interest in her young and the afterbirth, tongue-flicking and nosing them frequently. She grasped one neonate in her mouth and held it underwater for three minutes before releasing it unharmed (Holstrom, 1981). Townson (1985) observed copulation among captive *E. notaeus* from early October through mid-December, with parturition occurring early June through late August. Litters of 6, 11, 14, and 19 were recorded. Neonates fed on small live mice, chick legs or goldfish.

Tropidophis Species and Subspecies

Members of the genus *Tropidophis* occur in scattered localities on mainland South America, Greater Antilles, and Bahama Banks (McDowell, 1987).

Tropidophis are commonly referred to as wood snakes. In the majority of species adults range in size from only .3–1.0 m (1–3 ft) in total length. *Tropidophis* are primarily nocturnal and fossorial in nature.

Autohemorrhaging (spitting of blood) by *Tropidophis* species during handling has been reported by Mertens (1960), Hecht et al. (1955), Iverson (1986), and Tolson and Henderson (1993).

Other defensive behaviors include exuding a "musk" and coiling in a ball with the head protected in the center.

In captivity *Tropidophis* specimens typically require specific foods, such as small lizards and frogs. Neonates may require small lizards cut-up into pieces. Hornyak (pers. comm.) found that neonate *Tropidophis melanurus* maintained at the Toledo Zoological Gardens accepted *Eleutherodactylus* frog eggs and froglets as their first meals. Additional frog eggs were frozen in ice cube trays so that individual cubes of eggs could be thawed for subsequent feedings.

Hornyak (pers. comm.) noted captive neonate *Tropidophis melanurus* to be cannibalistic.

Bird and Reptile Litter works well as a substrate for *Tropidophis* enclosures. Hide areas which provide a "tight fit" for the snake should be provided. This can be accomplished by placing a small plastic hide box within a larger hide box enabling the boa to cram or wedge itself between the two hide boxes for a feeling of added security.

Mehrtens (1987) recommends maintaining most *Tropidophis* species within a temperature range of 26–29°C (80–85°F).

The Caicos Island dwarf boa (*Tropidophis greenwayi*) occurs on only six of the Caicos Islands—South Caicos, Middleton and Long Cays (off South Caicos), North Caicos, Middle Caicos, and Ambergris Cay (Iverson, 1986). The preferred habitat of this secretive boa consists of rocky coppice or dense scrub.

Tolson and Henderson (1993) report sexual maturity for *Tropidophis greenwayi lanthanus* is reached at 220–235 mm (9 in) snout-vent length, and a weight of 9.5–10.5 g in females, and about 8 g in males. Captive copulation has been observed from late January to late February, with parturition occurring early June. Ross and Marzec (1990) report a captive female *Tropidophis greenwayi* maintained at the Houston Zoo giving birth to a litter of four young in May. Bartlett (1990) reports that female *T. greenwayi lanthanus* give birth to one to three, 6 cm (2.5 in) long neonates.

The Haitian dwarf boa (*Tropidophis haetianus haetianus*) occurs in Cuba, Hispaniola and satellites, and Jamaica (Tolson and Henderson, 1993). Two births of *Tropidophis h. haetianus* were recorded at the Institute for Herpetological Research during November (Ross and Marzec, 1990). They noted that "litter sizes range from four to nine." Bartlett (1990) reports maintaining a wild-caught Haitian dwarf boa (*T. haetianus* subsp.) which gave birth to four young.

The Cuban dwarf boa (*Tropidophis melanurus*) is a large species, with a maximum total length of 1.06 m (41 in) (Tolson and Henderson, 1993). *Tropidophis melanurus* is a common species occurring throughout Cuba in a variety of habitats, from mesic (areas that are damp but not swampy) provinces of western Cuba to xeric (hot and dry) regions of southern Oriente Province (Tolson, 1980a).

Tolson (1980a) reports two births of *T. melanurus* from captive females. Parturition occurred on February 2 and February 26.

Bartlett (1990) reports captive female Bimini dwarf boas (*Tropidophis canus curtus*) giving birth to litters consisting of two or three 8 cm (3 in) long neonates.

Eyelash Boas (*Trachyboa boulengeri, Trachyboa gularis*)

The genus *Trachyboa* consists of two species of terrestrial, sedentary, nocturnal dwarf boas. Adult *Trachyboa* typically measure only 430 mm (17 in) in total length. *Trachyboa boulengeri* inhabits humid rain forest zones of Ecuador, Colombia, and Panama (Peters, 1960; Stimpson, 1969). *Trachyboa gularis* inhabits dry areas of coastal Ecuador. *T. boulengeri* possess distinctive small nasal and supraorbital horns.

Arnett et al. (1992) report maintaining a pair of *Trachyboa boulengeri* at an ambient temperature of 20–21°C (68–70°F). At this temperature the boas fed on live goldfish (*Carassius auratus*). The boas stopped feeding at temperatures above 21°C (70°F).

Lehmann (1970) reports a captive *Trachyboa boulengeri* voluntarily feeding on 3–5 cm (1–2 in) long grass frogs (*Rana temporaria*) and *Hyla aborea*. The majority of feeding occurred when the room was completely dark. Lehmann (1974) also reports captive *T. boulengeri* consuming live fish from the waterbowl, as well as dead fish (rudd (*Scardinius erythropthalmus*) and carp (*Carassius carassius*)) placed in the boa's enclosure during the night.

Lehmann (1970) observed a captive *T. boulengeri* giving birth to six young on October 24. This is consistent with Barbour (1937) noting six developed young within a dissected specimen from Panama. McLain (1983) reports that a female at the Houston Zoo contained five undeveloped embryos when it died. Marzec maintained a female *T. boulengeri* which gave birth to six viable young (Arnett et al., 1992).

Lehmann (1970) reported that the captive born neonate *T. boulengeri* voluntarily fed on 20–25 mm (½–1 in) reed frogs (*Hyperolius* spp.), and large *Hyperolius* tadpoles. Neonates began feeding prior to their first ecdysis, which occurred several months after birth.

Arnett et al. (1992) report captive *Trachyboa gularis* feeding on small live goldfish. *T. gularis* fed well at temperatures ranging from 25.6–28.5°C (78–83°F).

During the month of March a captive *T. gularis* gave birth to two live neonates and four infertile ova at the Cincinnati Zoo. An additional female gave birth in April to one live neonate and three dead embryos. Another live neonate was found with the female in May. (Arnett et al., 1992).

The neonate *T. gularis* fed shortly after birth on small guppies (*Lepistes reticulatus*). The neonates were housed individually in gallon jars with punctured lids for ventilation. The bottom of the jars contained approximately 5 mm (¼ in) of water, with paper towel for land space and hiding areas (Arnett et al., 1992).

Ungaliophis Species

The genus *Ungaliophis* is comprised of two species of dwarf boa. *Ungaliophis continentalis* is the northern form and inhabits low to intermediate elevations of the Pacific versant from Chiapas, Mexico, to Honduras, and also on the Caribbean versant of Chiapas (Wilson and Meyer, 1985). *Ungaliophis panamensis* is the southern form and occurs from southeastern Nicaragua through Costa Rica, Panama, and into northern Colombia. Adult *Ungaliophis* are typically only 50–70 cm (20–30 in) in total length and are thought to be primarily arboreal. Conant (1996) reports finding *Ungaliophis* in lowland tropical rain forests and pine forests.

Ungaliophis are a secretive boa and require arboreal hide areas. Ambient temperatures around 25°C (75°F) seem desirable for captive *Ungaliophis* (Burger, 1995). Burger (1995) reports captive *Ungaliophis* have fed on small frogs (*Acris*), *Anolis* lizards, and mice.

Ross and Marzec (1990) report three captive births. At the Houston Zoo a litter of six young was produced in May, and a second litter of five in June. A litter of five was born in June at the Reptile Breeding Foundation in Canada. Burger (1995) reports *Ungaliophis* litter sizes ranging from two to ten young, with an average of six. The Houston Zoo neonates accepted lizard parts as their first foods, while pink mice were accepted at the Reptile Breeding Foundation (Ross and Marzec, 1990).

Exiliboa placata

Exiliboa placata occurs in the Mexican state of Oaxaca, and inhabits cool montane cloud forests at elevations of 2000 m (6000 ft) or higher. *Exiliboa* is small and feeds on amphibians in the wild. This boid is very rare in captive collections, and has not been reproduced.

MADAGASCAR AND AFRICAN BOAS

Sand Boas (*Eryx* species)

Sand boas (genus *Eryx*) consists of 11 species and 14 subspecies (Ross and Marzec, 1990).

Sand boas are small (adults ranging from 46–122 cm (18–48 in) in total length), heavy-bodied constrictors with short tails and small heads. These cryptically colored burrowing boas are found in southeastern Europe, Africa, and western Asia, including Pakistan and India. Sand boas are cylindrical in shape with shovel-like snouts which aid in burrowing. The sand boa's small eyes are set toward the top of the head. This adaptation is especially beneficial as these boas spend large periods of time buried with only the eyes and nose protruding through the sand or loose soil.

In the wild, prey consists of small mammals, lizards, birds and even insects (Sorensen, 1987). Sand boas are primarily nocturnal and typically inhabit arid, semidesert areas (Welch, 1987).

Sexual dimorphism exists in certain species of sand boas such as *Eryx conicus* and *Eryx colubrinus,* with the females being considerably larger than the males. All sand boas are ovoviviparous. *Eryx tataricus* can produce as many as 34 young. Most species for which data exist breed biennially.

Captive husbandry for the commonly kept species of sand boas such as *E. conicus, E. colubrinus,* and *E. johni* seems to vary little from one species to the next (Ross and Marzec, 1990). The appropriate size terraria (38–76 l (10–20 gal)) provides suitable housing for most adult sand boas. Adults can also be maintained in transparent, shallow Rubbermaid tubs, as fossorial boas require little vertical space. Juveniles can be maintained in 9.5–19 l (2.5–5 gal) terraria, or in modified plastic shoebox or sweaterbox enclosures. A galvanized heat pad or heat tape should be located beneath one-third to one-half of the enclosure. It should be regulated to produce a substrate temperature of 27–32°C (80–90°F). A rheostat should be used with the heat source so that the temperature can be lowered slightly at night by reducing the electrical current. Year round nightly temperature drops are not a necessity for sand boa health or captive propagation. Enough relative humidity (minimum 50–65%) should be provided to insure proper shedding.

A substrate into which the snake can burrow is beneficial for sand boas, which are primarily fossorial in nature. Set-ups consisting of a paper or paper towel substrate and a hidebox are not suitable for sand boas. Sand or fine gravel is suitable although labor intensive to maintain. Other substrates including relatively dustless, finely processed wood products, such as Bird and Reptile Litter, or aspen bedding also work well. The substrate should cover the entire floor of the enclosure. A depth of 5–10 cm (2–4 in) is ideal for adult specimens. A small to medium (12–18 cm [5–7 in]) diameter, flat bottomed ceramic water bowl must be incorporated into the enclosure set-up. Sand boas will periodically drink from the bowl. The water bowl should rest completely on the enclosure floor as this will prevent boas from burrowing beneath it.

Neonate sand boas will typically feed on pink mice shortly after their first ecdysis. As growth is relatively rapid, within 2–3 months fuzzy mice can be fed to the juvenile. One week to ten day intervals between feedings is an adequate schedule for juveniles. A 10–14 day feeding schedule will suffice for adult specimens. Three to four week old mice are an ideal size to feed adult sand boas which are 60–90 cm (2–3 ft) in length. Mice should be offered in the evening. A food item can be placed in the enclosure just prior to the lights being turned off. With most individuals, freshly killed rodents will be accepted.

The most commonly maintained sand boa is the Kenyan (*Eryx colubrinus loveridgei*). The Kenyan sand boa occurs in the southern Somali Republic, Kenya, and northern Tanzania. *Eryx c. loveridgei* inhabits dry bush and semidesert areas. Sorensen (1988) reports 400 mm (15.5 in) for males and 655 mm (25.5 in) for females as adult lengths for *E. c. loveridgei*. Hedges (1983) states that a maximum size of 950 mm (40 in) is achieved by this subspecies.

The Kenyan sand boa is regularly reproduced in captivity by both zoological institutions and private individuals. McLain (1983) observed copulation among *Eryx c. loveridgei* during July and August, which resulted in a litter of eight young on December 28. He also noted copulation March through May of the following year, which resulted in two litters (of six and five) in September. McLain also mentions a female Kenyan sand boa "double clutching" by producing two litters within a period of 253 days. Goergen (pers. comm.) has observed copulation among *Eryx c. loveridgei* from early April through late May, with parturition occurring late July through late October. A litter of 15 viable young and one infertile ova was recorded by Goergen on August 14, 1984.

The nominate form *Eryx c. colubrinus* from northeastern Africa (commonly referred to as the Egyptian sand boa) is less frequently maintained in captivity than *Eryx c. loveridgei*. *Eryx c. colubrinus* is typically a problematic captive and is prone to respiratory disorders.

The rough-scaled sand boa (*Eryx conicus*) is a very popular species among herpetoculturists. *Eryx conicus* occurs in Pakistan and India. It inhabits sandy soil, rat burrows, brick piles, and rocky areas (Whitaker, 1978). Adult *Eryx conicus* measure 480 mm (18.7 in) for males and 940 mm (36.6 in) for females in total length (Sorensen, 1988).

I obtained a juvenile (2 week old) pair of *Eryx conicus* on August 25, 1989 from a private breeder. Both snakes fed shortly after being introduced into their new enclosures. Each of the boas has been housed individually in 38 L (10 gal) terraria with a full screen cover. A 7 cm (2 in) deep substrate of Bird and Reptile Litter was used. A 12 cm (5 in) diameter ceramic water bowl filled with clean water was accessible at all times. The ambient room temperature was maintained at 27–28°C (80–82°F), with a relative humidity of 75–80%. In addition the rear third of the terraria rested on a heat tape covered with 10 cm (4 in.) wide aluminum flashing for better heat dissipation, which allowed the boas access to a hot spot. The hot spot was typically utilized after feeding. It was also utilized when the boas were "in-the-blue" (nearing ecdysis). The heat tape was connected to an automatic timer which activated the tape in the morning, and turned it off at night.

A temperature cycling period was initiated early November 1992. This consisted of gradually reducing the ambient air temperature to 22–23°C (72–74°F) for 2 weeks. At the conclusion of this period, the ambient day temperature was gradually increased to 27°C (80°F). A nightly temperature drop to 22°C (72°F) was continued through mid-January. The heat tapes were discontinued during this cycling period. Goergen (pers. comm.) has successfully cycled *E. conicus* at temperatures of 18°C (65–68°F) for periods of 50–63 days.

The female *E. conicus* was moved to a 76 L (20 gal) terrarium with a Bird and Reptile Litter substrate, a full screen cover, and water bowl. I believed that the larger enclosure could better accommodate breeding activity. The male *E. conicus* was introduced into the female's enclosure late in November. Approximately 2 weeks later, the male was observed crawling along the back of the female, aligning his body with hers. During this interaction the female remained below the substrate. Copulation was observed in mid-December. During intromission both boas remained completely buried in the substrate with only their tails protruding at a 90 degree angle to the enclosure floor (this has been previously noted by McLain (1982) in the Kenyan sand boa, *Eryx colubrinus loveridgei*). After copulation, a galvanized metal heat pad was positioned beneath one half of the terrarium to provide additional heat for the female should it be desired. The heat pad operated 24 hours a day. During the gestation period the female would utilize this hot spot for as many as 12 hours at a time. This is typical behavior as additional heat is usually needed for proper development of boa young.

The female *E. conicus* never refused food during the gestation period. Small mice were fed at approximately 3–4 week intervals. The last meal offered was accepted only 2 weeks prior to giving birth. Parturition occurred April 23, 1993. Eight flawless neonates were discovered in the enclosure after the room lights were switched on. The number of young is consistent with other recorded births. The Memphis Zoo reported litters of nine and seven (Sorensen, 1988). Of 19 recorded litters the two largest consisted of 12 young (Goergen, pers. comm.)

Copulation was observed in the same single pair of *Eryx conicus* during January 1994, with both the male and female completely on top of the substrate during intromission. Parturition occurred June 6, 1994.

These breedings may have been unusual due to only one pair of *Eryx conicus* being involved. Using multiple males is beneficial for boa breeding, and usually greatly increases the chances of success. According to literature captive *Eryx conicus* give birth late May through August (Ross and Marzec, 1990). Goergen (pers. comm.) has recorded captive parturition dates from late May through mid-July, with the majority of observed copulations during mid-March. Wild *E. conicus* parturition has been recorded May through July (Whitaker, 1978) and June through August (Daniel, 1983). The April 23 birth may be noteworthy.

Madagascar Boas (*Acrantophis madagascariensis, Acrantophis dumerili, Sanzinia madagascariensis*)

Madagascar is a large island located off the southeast coast of Africa. Madagascar is home to many unusual and unique animal forms, including three endemic species of boa. The Madagascar boas are listed on Appendix I of the Convention on International Trade in Endangered Species of Wild Fauna and Flora (CITES). Although habitat destruction from slash-and-burn agriculture is the greatest threat to the Madagascar boas, reports as recent as 1988 state that *Acrantophis* skins are used for leather to support the tourist trade (Glaw and Vences, 1994).

Acrantophis inhabits dry forest areas of Madagascar. *Acrantophis madagascariensis* occurs in northern and western Madagascar, and also occurs on the island of Nosy Be. It has been collected in open deciduous woodland and been found sheltering in holes in river banks (Branch, 1982). *Acrantophis dumerili* occurs in the more arid regions of southwestern Madagascar.

Acrantophis madagascariensis is differentiated from *Acrantophis dumerili* primarily by its larger head scalation. See Figure 15. *Acrantophis madagascariensis* has six to 10 ocular scales, with *A. dumerili* having 11 to 16. *Acrantophis madagascariensis* is also larger with a specimen measuring 320 cm (10 ft) (Glaw and Vences, 1994). *Acrantophis dumerili* ranges in length from 125–145 cm (49–57 in).

Acrantophis madagascariensis has reproduced in captivity very infrequently. McKeown (1989) observed copulation among captive adult *A. madagascariensis* from late December through mid-February. A litter consisting of four viable young and two infertile ova was recorded August 17, after a gestation period of 226–234 days. A subsequent birth was recorded July 6, consisting of a single young (McKeown, pers. comm.). Cycling temperatures as low as 15.6°C (60°F) were utilized to achieve successful reproduction. Hamper (pers. comm.) recorded a litter of eight *A. madagascariensis*, born in July. McKeown (1989) recorded a total length of an *A. madagascariensis* at birth of 71.1 cm (28 in), and a weight of 285.9 g (10 oz).

An *Acrantophis madagascariensis* birth was recorded at the Gladys Porter Zoo, Brownsville, Texas, on March 24, 1974. The adult pair had been in captivity just over 8 months; therefore, it is very likely that the birth was the result of a wild mating prior to capture.

Huff (1984) reports captive copulation for specimens maintained in South Africa occurring from mid-May to September 1,

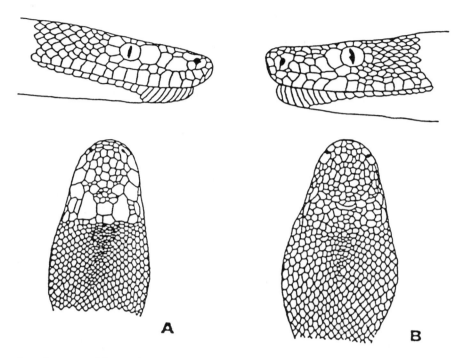

A=*Acrantophis madagascariensis*		B=*Acrantophis dumerili*
Head shields:	large	fragmented
Scales in loreal region:	2–3	4–5
Ocular scales:	6–10	11–16
Subcaudals:	37–41	31–35
Maximum length:	over 3 meters	under 2 meters

Figure 15 Distinguishing features of the genus *Acrantophis*. Illustrations and data from Branch, 1982. With permission.

with May 24 to August 5 being the most active period. Captive North American specimens breed 6 months later, as seasons are reversed between the Northern and Southern Hemispheres. Litter sizes of five recorded captive births range from two to six young. Total lengths of 55–64 cm (21–25 in), and weights of 156–212 g (5–7 oz) were recorded.

Branch (1982) reports captive *A. madagascariensis* maintained in South Africa copulate from March to August, with parturition occurring January through March, with litters of two to seven young being produced. Biennial births have been recorded by two females, even though mating occurred annually (Branch, 1982).

Branch and Erasmus (1976) observed copulation in a captive wild-caught pair of *A. madagascariensis* on 13 and 24 May. A litter of six young was produced February 21, 274–285 days after observed copulation. In addition a second wild-caught pair was observed copulating on August 5 and March 31. Four young were born after a gestation period of 238 days (it was not specified as to which of the matings resulted in young). Another wild-caught gravid *A. madagascariensis* collected in June gave birth to two young on February 26.

McKeown (pers. comm.) suggests maintaining *A. madagascariensis* under dry and low humidity conditions during the cycling period. A water bowl should only be placed in the enclosure for short periods, as cold and wet conditions can cause respiratory infections in this species.

McKeown (1989) states that after several months all neonates were feeding voluntarily on dead adult mice.

Acrantophis dumerili has been reproduced in captivity with more regularity than *A. madagascariensis*. Goergen (pers. comm.) has observed copulation among captive *A. dumerili* from late October through late March, with the majority of observed copulation occurring January through March. Parturition has occurred from late July through mid-October. A litter of 20 viable young and three infertile ova was recorded on September 20, 1991, with 12 males and 8 females being produced. Twenty (13 males and 7 females) young were produced by the same female on September 18, 1990. This female also produced 25 infertile ova on September 9, 1992.

A 17-year-old *A. dumerili* gave birth to seven viable young and six infertile ova. Parturition was approximately 2 to 3 weeks premature. The litter was this female's 11th consecutive season in which she produced viable young. (Goergen, pers. comm.).

The majority of captive *A. dumerili* will readily accept a diet of appropriately sized rodents. Huff (1984) mentions two specimens that only fed on birds. Some neonate *A. dumerili* will resist feeding initially, but after the first meal is accepted they typically become aggressive feeders. A substrate into which they can burrow, such as Bird and Reptile Litter, can often aid in neonate *A. dumerili* accepting their first meal by providing them with a sense of security.

Sanzinia is a monotypic genus consisting of *Sanzinia madagascariensis*. *Sanzinia* is widely distributed in Madagascar, being absent only from the sparse xerophyllous thicket of the extreme southwest (Branch, 1982). Andreone (1991) and Preston-Mafham (1991) report *Sanzinia* as being one of the most common snakes in Madagascar. Glaw and Vences (1994) also mention *Sanzinia* as being common, occurring in the primary and secondary forests, as well as in deforested areas. Western *Sanzinia* seem to differ in adult and juvenile color patterns from eastern specimens, with eastern adults possessing a greenish coloration. Young from the East coast are reddish, whereas young from Ambilobe (northwestern Madagascar) are brownish (Glaw and Vences, 1994). Adult coloration is typically reached at 5–6 months of age. Branch (1982) reports specimens from northwest Madagascar (Diego Suarez Province) as possessing an orange/yellow coloration.

Sanzinia is not as strictly arboreal as *Corallus* and spends much of its time on the ground. Andreone (1991) reports finding wild *Sanzinia* on the ground at night, often in lightly forested areas.

As a semi-arboreal species, climbing branches should be incorporated in the *Sanzinia* enclosure. Both substrate and overhead heat should be provided.

Most captive born *Sanzinia* will voluntarily feed on rodents. Branch and Erasmus (1976) report that some specimens show a marked preference for birds, rarely accepting mammals as food. Groves and Mellendick (1973) mention a juvenile *Sanzinia* that fed mainly on frogs and salamanders.

Goergen (pers. comm.) observed copulation among captive *Sanzinia* from early January through late April, with parturition occurring early September. A litter of 20 viable young with 16 males and 4 females was recorded on September 8, 1986. An additional litter consisting of one viable neonate, eight stillborn, and 12 infertile ova was recorded on September 7, 1988.

The low number of viable young in the 1988 litter is believed to have resulted from lack of sufficient substrate heat. Reproductive success was achieved utilizing a 35–40 day cycling period.

McLain (1984) observed copulation among captive *Sanzinia* from September to December, with parturition occurring mid-June through late July. Three litters were recorded: seven viable young, one stillborn, and two infertile ova; six young and five infertile ova; and one viable neonate, one stillborn, and 13 infertile ova.

Branch and Erasmus (1976) report two wild-caught gravid *Sanzinia* collected in July, giving birth to 10 young on December 30, and seven young on January 18.

Captive *Sanzinia* exhibit male combat as part of the mating ritual. Female *Sanzinia* coloration noticeably darkens during the gestation period. This phenomenon is possibly to allow for greater heat absorption to aid in the development of the young.

Round Island Boa (*Casarea dussumieri*)

Round Island lies just off the coast of Mauritius and is home to the Round Island Boa (*Casarea dussumieri*). *C. dussumieri* has become endangered due to habitat destruction caused by introduced goats.

In the wild *Casarea dussumieri* feed primarily on the Round Island skink (*Leiolopisma telfairii*) and Round Island Gecko (*Phelsuma guentheri*) (Bloxam, 1984). Bloxam (1980) reports that wild-caught Round Island boas initially proved difficult to feed, with the exception of accepting house geckos. The boas were gradually weaned onto pink mice by placing dead house geckos on top of the mice. The boas also accepted mice when smeared with chick. Eventually all captive specimens were successfully converted to a diet of young mice.

Bloxam and Tonge (1986) believe that there may be no distinct breeding season for *Casarea*. They have observed copulation among captive Round Island boas during most months of the year. Even though *Casarea dussumieri* is a boa, it is oviparous and clutches of three to 11 eggs have been recorded.

Neonate Round Island boas are brick-red in color and measure approximately 180 mm (7 in) in length. Neonate *Casarea* are difficult to rear in captivity. Providing a suitable diet is the most challenging aspect (Bloxam and Tonge, 1986).

Bloxam (pers. comm.) reports a reduction in the reproductive vigor of captive specimens, and believes that a diet of very young mice is inadequate for the female *Casarea* to develop a sufficient body weight during the breeding season. An artificial diet that is richer in calcium and provides additional bulk is being tried.

Casarea dussumieri may be the rarest boa and among the rarest snakes in the world. The Jersey Wildlife Preservation Trust and select zoos are the only facilities maintaining *Casarea*.

PACIFIC BOAS

Candoia Species and Subspecies

The genus *Candoia* is comprised of three species of small boa occurring through the South Pacific, from Papua, New Guinea, to Fiji. Sexually mature female *Candoia carinata paulsoni* are often less than 61 cm (2 ft) in total length. *Candoia b. bibroni* are larger, with males measuring as large as 122 cm (4 ft), and females as large as 2 m (6 ft) in total length (Ross and Marzec, 1990). *Candoia aspera* can grow to nearly 1 m (35 in).

Candoia carinata paulsoni occur in the Solomon Islands. Fauci (1979) reports copulation among captive specimens from April 20 through May 29. Parturition occurred November 2, with 27 young being produced. Additional litters were recorded on November 10, December 6, December 22, January 1, and January 5. The largest recorded litter consisted of 33 fully formed but stillborn young. Females were noted to be biennial breeders.

Fauci (1979) states that young *Candoia carinata paulsoni* fed 1–2 weeks after birth on small *Anolis* lizards, and day old pink mice.

Candoia aspera is a semi-aquatic boa which occurs in New Guinea and adjacent islands, the Bismarck Archipelago, and Solomon Islands. In the wild *C. aspera* feeds on lizards, frogs, and small mammals.

Copulation among captive *C. aspera* has been recorded in April, May, and September, with all copulations taking place in water. Parturition occurred in January with a litter of 22 young being produced (Ross and Marzec, 1990). A wild-caught gravid female measuring 734 mm (29 in) in total length, contained 18 developing young (Parker, n.d. [1982?]).

A wild-mated *Candoia bibroni australis* gave birth to eight young in May (Ross and Marzec, 1990).

Fauci (1979) has observed young *Candoia carinata paulsoni* feigning death or balling up as a defensive gesture.

I have successfully maintained *Candoia carinata* on an astroturf substrate with a hidebox; however, the majority of captive *Candoia* will benefit from a substrate into which they can burrow. Timmis (1969) observed that captive *Candoia aspera*, *Candoia bibroni*, and *Candoia carinata* refused all food until the enclosure floor was covered with a deep layer of dead leaves. The boas immediately buried themselves, leaving only the tips of their snouts protruding. The *Candoia* exhibited caudal luring to attract skinks and treefrogs which were subsequently ingested.

Most adult *Candoia* will voluntarily feed on rodents. Neonate and juvenile *Candoia* typically require lizards as their first meals, but can often be switched to pink mice by using scenting techniques described in the Food and Feeding chapter.

NORTH AMERICAN BOAS

Rosy Boas (*Lichanura trivirgata* subsp.) and Rubber Boas (*Charina bottae* subsp.)

The North American boas consist of rosy boas (*Lichanura trivirgata* subsp.) and rubber boas (*Charina bottae* subsp.). They are small, secretive, temperate climate boas, which are primarily fossorial in nature. Rosy boas occur in southwestern California and Arizona. The preferred habitat is desert and semi-desert scrub. Rubber boas occur from south central California north to southern Canada; east to Utah, Wyoming, Nevada, and Montana (Mehrtens, 1987). Suitable habitat consists of fallen logs, rock crevices, and burrows in damp meadows and woodlands.

Captive husbandry of the North American boas is fairly simple. Small glass terraria or plastic enclosures can comfortably house *Lichanura* or *Charina* species. A substrate into which they can burrow, such as Bird and Reptile Litter, should be provided. Hide areas should also be incorporated into the enclosure.

Most rosy boas will eagerly feed on the appropriate size mice. Mehrtens (1987) states at temperatures of 22–24°C (72–76°F) rubber boas will accept pre-killed mice. Reluctant rodent feeders can be offered small lizards or scented mice.

Captive propagation of the North American boas is considerably different than that of tropical boas in that the North American boas are hibernated and exposed to comparatively cooler temperatures for longer periods of time.

In North America hibernation should take place December through February. Not only is this the natural hibernation season for these North American boas, but it is also much easier to achieve cool temperatures for captives when outdoor temperatures are low.

Feeding should be discontinued in November at least 2 weeks prior to temperature reduction. Temperatures should be gradually reduced over a 2 week period. Hibernation should begin during December and consist of a constant temperature of 10–13°C (50–55°F) and should last approximately 90 days.

Hibernating North American boas in a room below ground (such as a basement) works well in temperate areas. Basements are naturally insulated by the earth and rarely drop below 10°C (50°F). The basement should have no major air leaks and temperatures should be monitored weekly and adjusted as necessary. Fresh water should be provided during the hibernation period. Heat should be provided gradually over a 2 week period in late February, after hibernation is completed. The boas should be fed two or three meals before introducing the sexes in a breeding attempt.

Hibernation is not recommended for any captives that are not sexually mature. Juveniles should be maintained in warm conditions and continue to feed on a routine schedule throughout winter. This will allow for slightly more rapid growth and sexual maturity can be reached (without excessive feeding) by 3 years of age. An exception to this would be a wild-caught juvenile boa which refuses food at the onset of the natural hibernation period, even though warm captive conditions are provided. North American boas which are underweight or in poor health should not be hibernated. It is better to miss a breeding attempt than to jeopardize the life of a specimen.

Spiteri (1993) reports that captive rosy boa gestation lasts about 120 days, with parturition typically occurring in September. At birth, neonates measure 30.5 cm (12 in) in total length. An average litter consists of five or six young, although a litter of 13 young was recorded (Spiteri, 1993). Goergen (pers. comm.) recorded litters of 19 and 17.

In the wild *Charina bottae* were observed copulating from April 16 through May 28 (Hoyer and Storm, 1991). Parturition occurred from early August through mid-October, with the majority of births occurring during the first 2 weeks of September.

LITERATURE CITED

Andreone, F. 1991. Conservation Aspects of the Herpetofauna of Mala-
gasy Rain Forests. Zoological Society "La Torbiera" - Scientific
Reports, No. 1. 45 pp.

Arnett, J. R., M. Goodwin, and H. R. Teagarden. 1992. *Trachyboa*
Peters in captivity: An overview. *In* Contributions to Herpetology.
Greater Cincinnati Herp. Soc: 91–94.

Barbour, T. 1910. Notes on the Herpetology of Jamaica. Bull. Mus.
Comparative Zool. 52(15): 272–301.

Barbour, T. 1937. Ovoviviparity in *Trachyboa*. Copeia 1937(2): 139.

Bartlett, R. D. 1990. Insular and "Dwarf" Boas of the New World.
Reptile and Amphibian Magazine, May/June 1990: 38–47.

Beebe, W. 1946. Field Notes on the Snakes of Kartabo, British Guiana,
and Caripito, Venezuela. Zoologica. (New York Zool. Soc.) 31(1):
11–52.

Blody, D. A., and D. T. Mehaffey. 1989. The reproductive biology of
the Annulated Boa, *Corallus annulatus*, in captivity. *In* International Zoo Yearbook No. 28: 167–172.

Bloxam, Q. M. C. 1977. Maintenance and breeding of the Jamaican
Boa, *Epicrates subflavus*, (Stejneger, 1901) at the Jersey Zoological
Park. The Dodo, No. 14: 69–73.

Bloxam, Q. M. C. 1980. Maintenance and breeding of Round Island
Herpetofauna. *In* Proc. 4th Annual Reptile Symposium on Cap-
tive Propagation & Husbandry: 50–69. Zoological Consortium,
Inc., Thurmont, MD.

Bloxam, Q. M. C. 1984. A preliminary report on the captive management and reproduction of the Round Island Boa, *Casarea
dussumieri*. *In* Proc. 7th Annual Reptile Symposium on Captive
Propagation & Husbandry: 115–123. Zoological Consortium,
Inc., Thurmont, MD.

Bloxam, Q. M. C., and S. J. Tonge. 1986. The Round Island Boa,
Casarea dussumieri, breeding programme at the Jersey Wildlife
Preservation Trust. The Dodo, No. 23: 101–107.

87

Branch, W. R. 1982. The status and captive breeding potential of African and Madagascan boids. *In* Proc. 6th Annual Reptile Symposium on Captive Propagation & Husbandry: 224–247. Zoological Consortium, Inc., Thurmont, MD.

Branch, W. R., and H. Erasmus. 1976. Reproduction in Madagascar ground and tree boas, *Acrantophis madagascariensis* and *Sanzinia madagascariensis*. *In* International Zoo Yearbook No.16: 78–80.

Buden, D. W. 1975. Notes on *Epicrates chrysogaster* (Serpents: Boidae) of the South Bahamas, With description of a new subspecies. Herpetologica 31(2): 166–177.

Burger, M. R. 1995. An arboreal burrower: The Dwarf Boa, *Ungaliophis*. The Vivarium 7(2): 46–49.

Chiras, S. 1979. Husbandry and reproduction of the Red Tail Boa, *Boa constrictor* spp. *In* Proc. 3rd Annual Reptile Symposium on Captive Propagation & Husbandry: 95–98. Zoological Consortium, Inc., Thurmont, MD.

Conant, R. 1966. A second record for *Ungaliophis* from Mexico. Herpetologica 22: 157–160.

Daniel, J. C. 1983. The Book of Indian Reptiles. Bombay Natural History Society. 141 pp.

Deschanel, J. P. 1978. Reproduction of anacondas, *Eunectes murinus*, at Lyons Zoo. *In* Int. Zoo Yearbook No. 18: 98–99.

de Vosjoli, P. 1990. The General Care and Maintenance of Red-Tailed Boas. Advanced Vivarium Systems, Lakeside, CA. 48 pp.

Ditmars, R. L. 1931. Snakes of the World. Macmillan Publishing Co., Inc., NY. 207 pp.

Fauci, J. 1979. Captive breeding and rearing of young of the Solomon Island Ground Boa, *Candoia carinata paulsoni*. *In* Proc. 3rd Annual Reptile Symposium on Captive Propagation & Husbandry: 91–94. Zoological Consortium, Inc., Thurmont, MD.

Fogel, D. 1992. The Importance of Patience. Notes from NOAH XIX(10): 4–5. Northern Ohio Association of Herpetologists, Cleveland.

Frye, F. L. 1981. Biomedical and Surgical Aspects of Captive Reptile Husbandry. Veterinary Medicine Publishing Co., Edwardsville, KS. 456 pp.

Funk, R. S. 1981. Intrabrood variation in boa and pythons. *In* Proc. 5th Annual Reptile Symposium on Captive Propagation & Husbandry: 17–29. Zoological Consortium, Inc., Thurmont, MD.

Funk, R. 1987. Implications of Cryptosporidiosis in Emerald Tree Boas, *Corallus caninus*. *In* Proc. 11th International Herpetological Symposia on Captive Propagation & Husbandry: 139–143. Zoological Consortium, Inc., Thurmont, MD.

Gillingham, J. C., C. C. Carpenter, B. J. Brecke, and J. B. Murphy. 1977. Courtship and copulatory behavior of the Mexican milk-snake *Lampropeltis triangulum sinaloae* (Colubridae). Southwest Nat. 22: 187–194.

Glaw, F., and M. Vences. 1994. A Fieldguide to the Amphibians and Reptiles of Madagascar. (Privately published, Cologne, Germany). 480 pp.

Groves, J. D. 1980. Observations and Comments on the Post-parturient Behavior of Some Tropical Boas of the Genus *Epicrates*. British Journal of Herpetology, 6: 89–92.

Groves, J. D., and J. A. Mellendick. 1973. Reproduction in the Madagascar tree boa, *Sanzinia madagascariensis*, at the Baltimore Zoo. *In* International Zoo Yearbook No. 13:106.

Hecht, M. K., V. Walters, and G. Ramm. 1955. Observations on the natural history of the Bahaman Pigmy Boa, *Tropidophis pardalis*, with notes on autohemorrhage. Copeia 1955(3): 249–251.

Hedges, N. G. 1938. Reptiles and Amphibians of East Africa. Nairobi: Kenya Literature Bureau. 139 pp.

Henderson, R. W. 1990. Tree boas on Grenada: The colorful puzzle. Bulletin of the Chicago Herp. Soc., 25(2): 21–24.

Henderson, R. W. 1991. Distribution and preliminary interpretation of geographic variation in the Neotropical tree boa, *Corallus enydris:* A progress report. Bulletin of the Chicago Herp. Soc., 26(5): 105–110.

Henderson, R. W., and R. A. Winstel. 1995. Aspects of habitat selection by an arboreal boa (*Corallus enydris*) in an area of mixed agriculture on Grenada. Journal of Herpetology, 29(2): 272–275.

Hine, R. A. 1989. Captive breeding of the Brazilian rainbow boa (*Epicrates cenchria cenchria*). *In* Breeding Reptiles & Amphibians: 125–132. British, Herpetological Society, London.

Holstrom, W. F., Jr. 1981. Observations on the reproduction of the yellow anaconda, *Eunectes notaeus*, at the New York Zoological Park. *In* Int. Zoo Yearbook No. 21: 92–94.

Hoyer, R. F., and R. M. Storm. 1991. Reproductive Biology of the Rubber Boa (*Charina bottae*). *In* Proc. 15th International Herpetological Symposium on Captive Propagation & Husbandry: 109–118. Int. Herpetological Symposium, Inc.

Huff, T. A. 1976. Breeding the Cuban Boa, *Epicrates angulifer*, at the Reptile Breeding Foundation. *In* Int. Zoo Yearbook No. 16: 81–82.

Huff, T. A. 1977a. Caging and Feeding Techniques Employed at the Reptile Breeding Foundation. *In* Proc. 2nd Annual Reptile Symposium on Captive Propagation & Husbandry: 15–19. Zoological Consortium, Inc., Thurmont, MD.

Huff, T. A. 1977b. Captive propagation and husbandry of *Epicrates* at the Reptile Breeding Foundation. *In* Proc. 2nd Annual reptile Symposium on Captive Propagation & Husbandry: 103–112. Zoological Consortium, Inc., Thurmont, MD.

Huff, T. A. 1978. Breeding the Puerto Rican Boa, *Epicrates inornatus*, at the Reptile Breeding Foundation. *In* Int. Zoo Yearbook No. 18: 96–97.

Huff, T. A. 1979. Some Parameters for Breeding Boids in Captivity. *In* Proc. 3rd Annual Reptile Symposium on Captive Propagation & Husbandry: 84–90. Zoological Consortium, Inc., Thurmont, MD.

Huff, T. A. 1980. Captive Propagation of the Subfamily Boinae with Emphasis on the Genus *Epicrates*. *In* Reproductive Biology and Diseases of Captive Reptiles: 125–134. Society for the Study of Amphibians and Reptiles. Ithaca, N.Y.

Huff, T. A. 1984. The Husbandry and Propagation of the Madagascar Ground Boa (*Acrantophis dumerili*) in Captivity. Acta Zoologica et Pathologica Antverpiensia. Bulletins de le Societe Royale De Zoologie D'Anvers, Antwerp. Nov. 1984, No. 78: 255–270.

Iverson, J. B. 1986. Notes on the natural history of the Caicos Island Dwarf Boa, *Tropidophus greenwayi*. Caribbean Jour. Sci. 22(3–4): 191–198.

Kluge, A. G. 1991. Boine snake phylogeny and research cycles. Miscellaneous Publications, Museum of Zoology, University of Michigan, Ann Arbor, No. 178. 58 pp.

Langhammer, J. K. 1983. A new subspecies of Boa constrictor, *Boa constrictor melanogaster*, from Ecuador (Serpents: Boidae). Tropical Fish Hobbyist 32(4): 70–79.

Laszlo, J. 1975. Probing as a practical method of sex recognition in snakes. *In* Int. Zoo Yearbook No. 15: 178–179.

Laszlo, J. 1979. Notes on Reproductive Patterns of Reptiles in Relation to Captive Breeding. *In* Int. Zoo Yearbook No. 19: 22–27.

Laszlo, J. 1984. Further Notes on Reproductive Patterns of Amphibians and Reptiles in Relation to Captive Breeding. *In* Int. Zoo Yearbook No. 23: 166–174.

Lazell, J. D., Jr. 1964. The Lesser Antillean Representatives of *Bothrops* and *Constrictor*. Bulletin of the Museum of Comparative Zoology, Harvard Univ., 132(3): 245–273.

Lehmann, H. D. 1970. "Beobachtungen bei der Haltung und Aufzucht von *Trachyboa boulengeri* (Serpentes, Boidae)" in Salamandra 6(1/2): 32–42. [Translation *in* Bull. Chicago Herp. Soc. 28(2): 25–30, 1993].

Lehmann, H. D. 1974. "*Trachyboa boulengeri* (Serpentes, Boidae) frißt

Fische" in Salamandra 10(3/4): 132–133 [Translation *in* Bull. Chicago Herp. Soc. 28(2): 30–31, 1993].

Lynn, W. G., and C. Grant. 1940. The Herpetology of Jamaica. The Institute of Jamaica. Kingston. 148 pp.

McDowell, S. B. 1987. Geographic Distribution: Problems in Phlyogeny and Zoogeography. *In* Snakes: Ecology and Evolutionary Biology: 77–105. MacMillan Publishing Co., New York.

McKeown, S. 1989. The First Captive Breeding of the Madagascar Ground Boa (*Acrantophis madagascariensis*) in North America From Long Term Adults. *In* Captive Propagation and Husbandry of Reptiles and Amphibians: 69–76. Northern California Herp. Soc. Special Publication #5.

McLain, J. M. 1982. Reproduction in Captive Kenyan Sand Boas, *Eryx colubrinus loveridgei*. *In* Proc. 5th Annual Reptile Symposium on Captive Propagation & Husbandry: 76–82. Zoological Consortium, Inc., Thurmont, MD.

McLain, J. M. 1983. Notes on Boid Reproduction at the Houston Zoological Park. *In* Proc. 6th Annual Reptile Symposium on Captive Propagation & Husbandry: 248–264. Zoological Consortium, Inc., Thurmont, MD.

McLain, J. M. 1984. Reproduction in Captive Malgasy Tree Boas, *Sanzinia madagascariensis* (Serpentes: Boidae). *In* Proc. 7th Annual Reptile Symposium on Captive Propagation & Husbandry: 124–131. Zoological Consortium, Inc., Thurmont, MD.

Mehrtens, J. M. 1987. Living Snakes of the World in Color. Sterling Publishing Co., Inc. New York. 480 pp.

Mengden, G., C. G. Platz, R. Hubbard, and H. Quinn. 1980. Semen Collection, Freezing and Artificial Insemination in Snakes. *In* Reproductive Biology and Diseases of Captive Reptiles. Society for the Study of Amphibians and Reptiles. Ithaca, N.Y.

Mertens, R. 1960. The World of Amphibians and Reptiles. George G. Harrap & Co. Ltd., London. 207 pp.

Mitchell, A. W. 1986. The Enchanted Canopy. William Collins, Great Britain. 255 pp.

Moyle, M, and R. A. Ross. 1991. Problems Encountered With the Husbandry of the Emerald Tree Boa, *Corallus caninus*. *In* Proc. 15th International Herpetological Symposium on Captive Propagation & Husbandry: 119–126. International Herpetological Symposium, Inc.

Murphy, J. B., and R. K. Guese. 1977. Reproduction in the Hispaniolan Boa, *Epicrates fordii fordii* at the Dallas Zoo. *In* Int. Zoo Yearbook No. 17: 132–133.

Neill, W. T., and R. Allen. 1962. Parturient anaconda, *Eunectes gigas* Latreille, eating own abortive eggs and foetal membranes. Quarterly Journal of the Florida Academy of Sciences 25: 73–75.

Nelson, P. 1994. Night at the Place of the Killings. National Wildlife 32(3): 46–49.

Parker, F. (n.d.[1982]). The Snakes of Western Province. Wildlife in Papua New Guinea No. 82/1. Konedobu. 78 pp.

Peters, J. A. 1960. The snakes of Ecuador. Bull. Mus. Comp. Zool. 122(9): 491–541.

Peters, J. A., and B. Orejas-Miranda. 1970. Catalog of the Neotropical Squamata: Part 1. Snakes. Bulletin US National Museum 297. 347 pp.

Perez-Santos, C., and A. G. Moreno. 1988. Ofidios de Colombia. Museo Regionale di Scienze Naturali-Torino. 517 pp.

Preston-Mafham, K. 1991. Madagascar: A Natural History. Facts-On-File, Inc., New York. 224 pp.

Price, R. M., and P. Russo. 1991. Revisionary comments on the genus *Boa* with the description of a new subspecies of *Boa constrictor* from Peru. The Snake 23(1): 29–35. Japan Snake Institute.

Retes, F. 1992. A non-scientific (behavioral) approach to reptile reproduction. *In* Collected Papers of the Tucson Herp. Society: 61–64.

Ross, R. A. 1989. Regurgitation Syndrome in Boid Snakes. *In* Proc. 13th International Symposium on Captive Propagation & Husbandry: 81–85. International Herpetological Symposium, Inc.

Ross, R. A., and G. Marzec. 1990. The Reproductive Husbandry of Pythons and Boas. The Institute for Herpetological Research, Stanford, CA. 270 pp.

Schmidt, K. P., and R. F. Inger. 1957. Living Reptiles of the World. Doubleday & Co., Inc. Garden City, N.Y. 287 pp.

Schwartz, A., and R. W. Henderson. 1991. The Amphibians and Reptiles of the West Indies: Descriptions, Distributions, and Natural History. Univ. Florida Press. Gainesville. 720 pp.

Smith, H. M. 1943. Summary of the collections of snakes and crocodilians made in Mexico under the Walter Rathbone Bacon Travelling Scholarship. Proc. U.S. National Museum, 93: 349–504.

Snider, A. T., and J. K. Bowler. 1992. Longevity of Reptiles and Amphibians in North American Collections. Society for the Study of Amphibians and Reptiles, Herpetological Circular No. 21. 40 pp.

Sorensen, D. 1987. Behavior and Reproduction in the Genus *Eryx*. *In* Proc. 11th International Herpetological Symposium on Captive Propagation and Husbandry: 125–135. Zoological Consortium, Inc., Thurmont, MD.

Sorensen, D. 1988. The Genus *Eryx*. Bulletin of the Chicago Herpetological Society. 23(2): 21–25.

Spiteri, D. G. 1993. The current taxonomy and captive breeding of the Rosy Boa (*Lichanura trivirgata*). The Vivarium 5(3): 18–19, 27.

Stimson, A. F. 1969. Boidae. *In* Liste der rezenten Amphibien und Reptilien. Das Tierreich, Liferung 89: 2–4. Walter de Gruyter, Berlin.

Strimple, P. D. 1986. Captive propagation of the green anaconda, *Eunectes murinus murinus* (Linnaeus). The Forked Tongue 11(6): 5–9. Greater Cincinnati Herp. Soc.

Strimple, P. D. 1993. Overview of the natural history of the green anaconda (*Eunectes murinus*). *In* Herpetological Natural History 1(1): 25–35. International Herpetological Symposium, Inc.

Strimple, P. D. 1994. The Husbandry of juvenile green anacondas (*Eunectes murinus*) in captivity. The Vivarium 6(1): 52–54.

Tepedelen, K. 1989. Captive Propagation in the Emerald Tree Boa (*Corallus caninus*). *In* Captive Propagation and Husbandry of Reptiles and Amphibians: 77–80. Northern California Herpetological Society, Davis, CA.

Timmis, W. H. 1969. Observations on Pacific Boas, *Candoia* spp. at Sydney Zoo. *In* Int. Zoo Yearbook No. 9: 53.

Tolson, P. J. 1980a. Captive Propagation and Husbandry of the Cuban Dwarf Boa, *Tropidophis melanurus*, at the Museum of Zoology, The University of Michigan. *In* Proc. 4th Annual Reptile Symposium on Captive Propagation & Husbandry: 43–46. Zoological Consortium, Inc., Thurmont, MD.

Tolson, P. J. 1980b. Captive Reproductive Behavior in Four Species of the Boid Genus *Epicrates*. *In* Proc. 4th Annual Reptile Symposium on Captive Propagation & Husbandry: 87–97. Zoological Consortium, Inc., Thurmont, MD.

Tolson, P. J. 1988. Critical Habitat, Predator pressures, and Management of *Epicrates monensis* on the Puerto Rico Bank: A Multivariate Analysis. U.S. Dept. Agric. Forest Serv. Gen. Tech. Rep., RM-166: 228–238.

Tolson, P. J. 1989. Breeding the Virgin Islands Boa, *Epicrates monensis granti*, at the Toledo Zoological Gardens. *In* Int. Zoo Yearbook No. 28: 163–167.

Tolson, P. J. 1992. The Reproductive Biology of the Neotropical Boid Genus *Epicrates* (Serpents: Boidae). *In* Reproductive Biology of South American Vertebrates:165–178. Springer-Verlag, N.Y.

Tolson, P. J. 1994. The Reproductive Management of the Insular species of *Epicrates* (Serpentes: Boidae) in Captivity. *In* Captive Management and Conservation of Amphibians and Reptiles:

353–357. Society for the Study of Amphibians and Reptiles. Ithaca, N.Y.

Tolson, P. J., and R. W. Henderson. 1993. The Natural History of West Indian Boas. R & A Publishing Limited, Middlesex, England. 125 pp.

Townson, S. 1985. The Captive Reproduction and Growth of the Yellow Anaconda (*Eunectes notaeus*). *In* Reptiles: Breeding, Behaviour and Veterinary Aspects: 33–43. British Herpetological Society, London.

Wagner, E. 1985. Captive husbandry of wild-caught Emerald Tree Boas. *In* Captive Propagation and Husbandry of Reptiles and Amphibians: 109–111. Northern California Herpetological Society, and Bay Area Amphibian and Reptile Society, Davis, CA.

Walsh, T. 1979. *Corallus canina* at the National Zoo. Unpublished manuscript, 21 pages.

Walsh, T. 1994. Husbandry of Long-term Captive populations of Boid Snakes (*Epicrates, Corallus*, and *Chondropython*). *In* Captive Management and Conservation of Amphibians and Reptiles: 359–362. Society for the Study of Amphibians and Reptiles. Ithaca, N.Y.

Walsh, T., and B. Davis. 1983. Husbandry and breeding of the Brazilian Rainbow Boa, *Epicrates cenchria*, at the National Zoological Park. *In* Proc. 7th Annual Reptile Symposium on Captive Propagation & Husbandry: 108–114. Zoological Consortium, Inc. Thurmont, MD.

Weidner, T. M. 1986. Captive Reproduction of Emerald Tree Boas, *Corallus caninus* Linnaeus. *In* Proc. 10th International Herpetological Symposium on Captive Propagation & Husbandry: 127–134. Zoological Consortium, Inc., Thurmont, MD.

Welch, K. R. G. 1987. Handbook on the Maintenance of Reptiles in Captivity. Robert E. Krieger Publishing Co., Malabar, FL. 156 pp.

Wells, E. 1980. A diurnal variation's effect on a captive breeding of a *Boa constrictor constrictor*. *In* Proc. 4th Annual Reptile Symposium on Captive Propagation & Husbandry: 11–16. Zoological Consortium, Inc., Thurmont, MD.

Whitaker, R. 1978. Common Indian Snakes. A Field Guide. Macmillan, India Limited. 154 pp.

Wilson, L. D., and J. R. Meyer. 1985. The Snakes of Honduras. Milwaukee Public Museum. 150 pp.

Winstel, A. 1989. Herpetoculture of the Amazon Tree Boa. The Vivarium 1(4):12–14.

COMMON NAME
AND SUBJECT INDEX

SCIENTIFIC NAME INDEX